ALL KINDS OF
TRUCKS

BY EDITH T. KUNHARDT
ILLUSTRATED BY ART SEIDEN

A GOLDEN BOOK · NEW YORK

WESTERN PUBLISHING COMPANY, INC., RACINE, WISCONSIN 53404

Copyright © 1984 by Western Publishing Company, Inc. Illustrations copyright © 1984 by Art Seiden. All rights reserved. Printed in the U.S.A. No part of this book may be reproduced or copied in any form without written permission from the publisher. GOLDEN®, GOLDEN & DESIGN®, and A GOLDEN BOOK® are trademarks of Western Publishing Company, Inc. Library of Congress Catalog Card Number: 83-82601. ISBN 0-307-10406-0/ISBN 0-307-60403-9 (lib. bdg.)   A B C D E F G H I J

It is early morning. The sky is getting light. The milk truck is here. It brings fresh milk and eggs and butter for breakfast.

Every day the bakery truck delivers fresh bread
and rolls and cakes and pies to restaurants and stores.
The inside of the truck smells like warm bread.

Garbage and trash get thrown into the back of the garbage truck. The truck works hard to push its metal squeezer. The squeezer crushes boxes and cartons so that more garbage can fit in.

The automobile carrier hauls new cars from the automobile factory. It takes them to places where they will be sold. The cars look funny riding along with no drivers.

The gasoline truck brings gasoline to fill up the big tank under the gas station. Then the pump pumps the gas out of the tank and into the car.

The cement mixer's tank turns around and
around. The cement inside the tank will get hard
if it stops moving.

It is time to make a new sidewalk. Down the
slide comes the cement. The workers spread it
out fast.

The tow truck has come to get a broken car.
The winch pulls the front of the car up in the air.
Now the truck will tow the car to the garage.

The farmer loads his pickup truck. He hopes
his giant pumpkin will win a prize at the fair.

Ding! Ding! The ice cream truck's bell is ringing. Ice cream cups, cones, and ices are for sale. When the freezer is opened, frosty air comes out.

Five horses go up the ramp of the horse van. Inside the van, they walk backward into their stalls. They are traveling to a horse show out of town. If they get hungry on the way, they can eat hay out of nets hanging from the ceiling.

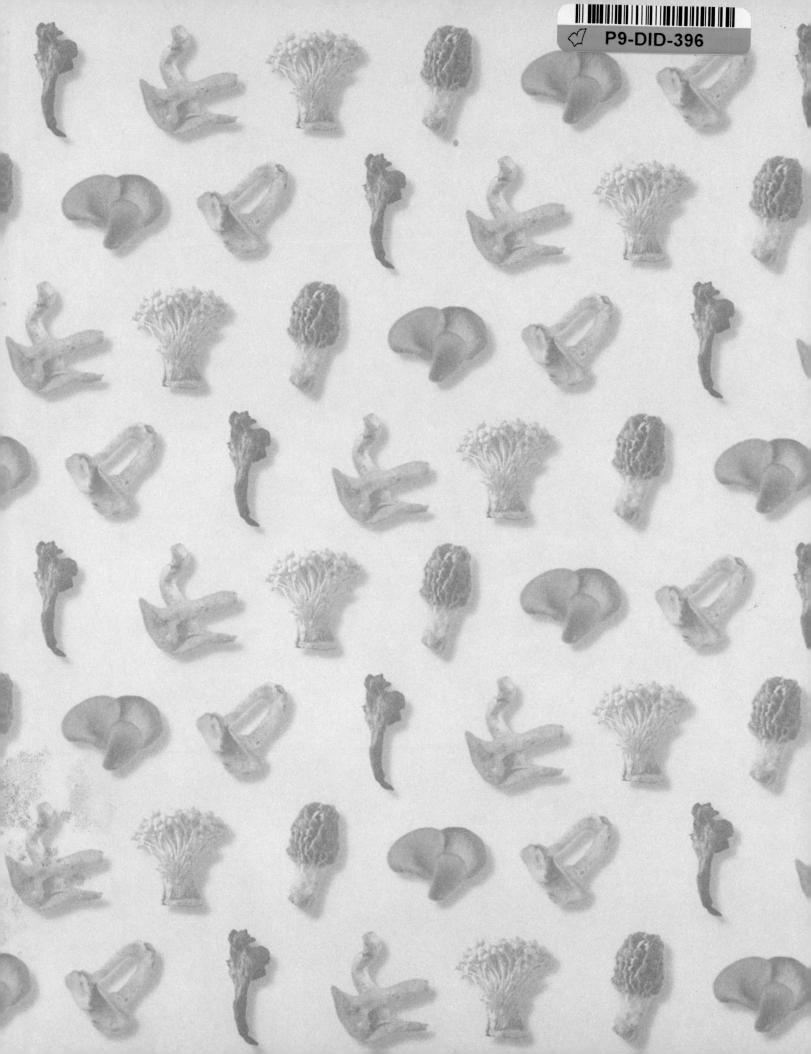
P9-DID-396

a FEAST of
MUSHROOMS

a FEAST of
MUSHROOMS

MARLENA SPIELER

CHARTWELL
BOOKS, INC.

A QUINTET BOOK

Published by **Chartwell Books**
A Division of Book Sales, Inc.
114, Northfield Avenue
Edison, New Jersey 08837

This edition produced for sale in the U.S.A.,
its territories and dependencies only.

Copyright © 1998 Quintet Publishing Limited.

All rights reserved. No part of this publication may be
reproduced, stored in a retrieval system or transmitted
in any form or by any means, electronic, mechanical,
photocopying, recording or otherwise, without the
permission of the copyright holder.

ISBN 0-7858-0897-3

This book was designed and produced by
Quintet Publishing Limited
6 Blundell Street
London N7 9BH

Creative Director: Richard Dewing
Art Director: Clare Reynolds
Designer: Steve West
Senior Editor: Sally Green
Editor: Rosie Hankin
Photographer: Philip Wilkins
Food Stylist: Jenny Stacey

Typeset in Great Britain by
Central Southern Typesetters, Eastbourne
Manufactured by
Pica Colour Separation Overseas Ptd Ltd.
Printed in Singapore by
Star Standard Industries (Pte.) Ltd.

Contents

Acknowledgments

Thank you to my family for their support. To my parents, Caroline and Izzy Smith, who never touch mushrooms, to my grandmother Sophia Dubowsky, and to Aunt Estelle, Uncle Sy, and all my cousins who eat mushrooms heartily. To Jon and Leah, for really liking mushrooms, and to my husband, Alan, who conducts his own inimitable forays through life with and without mushrooms.

To all the friends who have sat at my table and eaten mushrooms, or who have bought me mushrooms as gifts from far-flung places, including Sri and Roger Owen, whose hospitality is legendary; Sue Kreitzman; Paul Richardson; Alexa Stace; Fred and Mary Barclay; Nigel Patrick; Graham Ketteringham; Jerome Freeman; Sheila Hannon; Dr. Esther Novak and the Rev. John Chendo; M. A. Mariner; Sandy Waks, for her gift of shiitakes; Kamala Friedman; Amanda Hamilton and Tim Hemmeter; and to Rachel Edelson, for the fresh porcini toted in her carry-on bag from Tuscany as a delicious dinner that night. To Gretchen, just because.

To the *San Francisco Chronicle* for commissioning an article on wild mushrooms that started me writing about them in earnest. Thank you to my good-natured agent, Borra Garson, and also to Stefanie Foster who commissioned this book.

A huge thank you to Geoff Rowe, the 'Mushroom Man' of Borough market, for his wonderful wild, exotic, and cultivated mushrooms. And to Harvey Nicols and Thomas and Thomas in London, England, for their excellent dried mushrooms. The publishers would also like to thank Harrods Food Hall, London, England, for the supply of wild mushrooms used in photography.

Picture credits: p.9, Travel Ink/Simon Reddy; p.10, Life File; p.11, p.13, The Mushroom Bureau.

Preface

I was a late bloomer as a mushroom lover. As a child I avoided them assiduously. Though I loved to see them growing in the fields, I did not want to eat them. They frightened me. I was sure that elves and nymphs lived beneath them. My parents warned me as a child not to eat wild mushrooms or toadstools, but even cultivated mushrooms were no good. I was convinced there was something very odd about these things that grew in the dirt and the dark—I just didn't trust them and I wasn't going to eat them.

Then, as a teenager, I lived on a kibbutz with a group of young French people. One spring afternoon they unearthed a cache of field mushrooms. A celebration was planned and a campfire made. The mushrooms were picked, washed, and prepared, and then sautéed in butter before being

combined with scrambled egg. They were the most delicious thing I have ever tasted. The mushrooms were foresty and tender, and smelled as rich as they tasted.

From then on I have eaten every fungus that has come my way, including exquisite porcini and oh-so-expensive truffles, about which I am inordinately greedy. I was once even attacked by a large pig at an agricultural show in Paris, as I was carrying a package in my bag filled with a truffle—a generous gift from a fellow fungi fanatic.

Marlena

Introduction

Mushrooms are members of the simple plants known as the fungi family, which also includes truffles, puff-balls, tree cloud fungus, and other edible fungi. They reproduce by spores, single-celled bodies that are scattered by the wind. This allows mushrooms to propagate themselves wherever the climate and location is suitable, and means that many mushrooms are eaten in a number of countries but are known by different names.

Most mushrooms are 90 percent water and, depending on the type, contain various minerals—including phosphorus, potassium, iron, copper, zinc, selenium, and salt—plus vitamins, such as B1 (thiamin), B2 (riboflavin), niacin, pantothenic acid, folic acid, B12, C, and D. They are low in calories in their raw state, containing about 7 calories per ounce, and low in fat, having 2–3 percent fat depending on the variety. Mushrooms contain a respectable amount of protein, at around 3–9 percent, again depending on type. This protein is second only in quality to beans, peas, and lentils in its amino acid content, and between 70 and 90 percent of the protein can be easily digested.

Many medical herbalists and practitioners of Eastern medicine maintain that mushrooms, especially shiitake mushrooms, can boost the immune system. They are therefore held to be useful in the treatment of such diseases as cancer and Aids.

Whereas once our supermarkets sold only the little cultivated mushrooms we are so familiar with, today a dazzling range of wild and cultivated mushrooms is available. Any good-size supermarket should be able to offer a choice of fresh and dried mushrooms that was once only provided by specialty outlets.

Some mushrooms that are labeled "wild" are in actual fact cultivated, including shiitake and

A dazzling range of wild and cultivated mushrooms is available today.

Mushrooms on sale in La Boqueria Market, Barcelona, Spain.

oyster mushrooms. I prefer to call these "tamed," though the more common term for them is "exotic." Mushrooms come in many colors, from beige and brown, through inky black and steel-gray, through yellow and pink. Their aromas range from sweet and musky, through slightly dank and provocatively stinky, through clean and crisp.

Mushrooms are an important part of French life. During the fungi season, a French market is a thrilling sight to the mushroom enthusiast, with lush, fresh mushrooms piled up into multicolored heaps. The Cours Selaya market in Nice is as confusing as it is alluring. I have often gotten overwhelmed trying to choose and have just ended up pointing here, there, and there almost in a panic, then trotting home with my cache, though first spending a few moments to ask the vendor what he or she might recommend. This is the best way to discover more about mushrooms.

Mushrooms have, of course, long been an important part of eating in France. Any restaurant worth its *vin et pain* will celebrate the *champignon*. The French were the first to cultivate mushrooms, in the late 1890s, so that the population could enjoy this lusty vegetable. Today, mushroom hunting is such a popular pastime that, during the season, pharmacies throughout

France will have a mycologist on their staff to help people identify their finds. This helps to avoid upset stomachs etc.

In North America, spring is the chief season for hunting wild mushrooms, although in mild climates, they can be found almost year-round. Morels are the main mushrooms to be found at this time of year. They sprout up across the width of the country, often under apple and oak trees, and the northern Midwest has morel festivals in the spring. Porcini also grow throughout North America at this time, and in places with mild climates such as California and Oregon, they have a spring season and a fall season. Chanterelles can be found in the woods in summer and fall, usually golden chanterelles, but sometimes white. Trompette de la mort, although not as common, can also be found across the country. Chicken-of-the-Woods are rare, but do grow on trees in New England and the Pacific Northwest. The forests of this region also produce about 20 varieties of edible wild mushrooms, including all of the above, plus the puff-ball, oyster, and lobster mushrooms.

However, mushroom hunting should not be undertaken lightly. I do not recommend hunting, however exciting it may seem, unless you are accompanied by an expert—someone experienced enough and qualified literally to take your life into his or her hands. Looking through a guide to mushrooms is not enough, even if it is a field guide written by an absolute expert. The differences between poisonous and edible mushrooms can be difficult to spot, and confusing even to the experienced mycologist. Some mushroom hunters I know specialize in only one fungus in an attempt to avoid errors. There is an old saying that there are old mushroom hunters and daring mushroom hunters, but no old, daring mushroom hunters. It must be remembered that every year people die from eating wrongly identified mushrooms.,

Even some varieties that are generally deemed safe may trigger unpleasant or dangerous reactions in some people, so if you are trying a mushroom for the first time, try not to be greedy and only eat a little. The way you store mushrooms can also affect their safety. If you have carried a mixed basket home from a hunting expedition, the unsafe ones may have tainted the innocuous varieties by their spores, and toxins can develop during transportation.

Treat mushrooms with the respect they deserve, obtain them from safe sources, store, prepare, and cook them properly, and you can only enjoy their wonderful aroma, texture, and taste.

Chanterelles can be found in the woods in summer and fall. They are usually golden in colour.

Easy Recipe

Green Beans or Young Asparagus with Spring Mushrooms and Truffle Oil

Steam some young pencil-thin green beans or young asparagus until bright green and just tender. Drain and refresh in cold water. Sauté several shallots and a garlic clove, chopped with a handful of mushrooms cut into bite-size pieces—choose from chanterelles, morels, trompette de la mort, and/or porcini. Spoon the mushrooms over the green beans or asparagus and serve immediately with a few drops of truffle oil drizzled over.

Easy Recipe

Roasted hedgehog Fungus

Preheat a 375°F oven. Arrange a single layer of hedgehog fungus or any other mushroom you like in a pan and toss with chopped garlic, olive oil or butter, and salt to taste. Drizzle with some stock, then roast in the oven for about 30 minutes, depending on the type of mushroom(s) you are using. Serve, with chopped parsley or snipped chives scattered over, as an accompaniment for any meat dish, on top of fettucine tossed with cream and a little coarsely shredded Parmesan, or as part of a vegetarian meal.

Chicken Accompaniment Serve any mushroom, or combination of mushrooms, sautéed, alongside a succulent roasted chicken.

Commercially Available Mushrooms and Fungi

Black Fungus, Cloud Ears, Tree Fungus

Available dried, this fungus expands dramatically to a frilly, earlike object once rehydrated. Delicious in stir-fries, soups, and fillings, it is more a texture than a flavor. This texture may take some getting used to, but, once you have acquired a taste for these black fungi, they can be nearly addictive. They are chewy and crunchy at the same time, and different than almost anything else. And the Chinese believe that they are extremely good for you, contributing to a long life.

This delicious, though quite delicate and bland, fungus is available from some Asian stores and comes in two types: large and small. The large variety is thicker and coarser in texture than the small one, which is considered superior, being finer textured and tastier.

To Prepare Pour just boiling water over the fungus in a bowl. Cover, and leave to soak for a half hour or until it has puffed up. Leave to cool in the water. When cool enough to handle, take the fungus out, trim off and discard the tough stem ends, and prepare as required for your recipe. Unlike other mushrooms' soaking liquid, the liquid from this fungus does not have a particularly strong or fine scent or flavor. It is usually discarded, or I sometimes add it to shiitake mushroom liquid for soups.

Brown Mushroom

Similar to the common cultivated mushroom, the brown mushroom is often slightly larger than the ordinary button mushroom, and has a pale straw-brown outside color with a slightly strong, more mushroomy, flavor. They are sometimes called cremini, and are available fresh.

To Prepare Wipe the outside with a damp cloth or paper towel. Prepare and cook as desired. These mushrooms are good quickly sautéed, braised, stir-fried, or simmered.

Button Mushroom See Cultivated, or Common, Mushrooms.

Cep, Penny Bun See Porcini.

Brown mushrooms

Champignon, Field Mushroom

This simple little mushroom, *Agaricus campestris*, is the most commonly found and picked wild mushroom. It is quite similar to the ordinary commercial, cultivated mushroom, but has a bit more flavor. It is available fresh and, less commonly, dried. There is also the horse mushroom, *Agaricus arvensis*, with a stronger, fennel-like flavor.

To Prepare Brush any dirt off or wipe with a damp cloth or paper towel. Trim the tough stem ends and discard. Use champignons wherever you would use porcini, even though their flavor is a bit milder. They make a delicious addition to foresty soups, or may be sautéed, braised, or used in sauces. When small, they may be eaten raw.

The Field mushroom is the most commonly found and picked mushroom.

Chanterelle (Canthatellus)

You'll find the chanterelle mostly in the fall and winter. A delicate, wild variety, it comes in a wide range of types. There is the yellow chanterelle, a trumpet-shaped, very attractive mushroom, with an apricot scent. There is also the white chanterelle, the pig ear, the black chanterelle, and the horn of plenty (also known, slightly alarmingly, as *trompette de la mort*—and how it is referred to in this book) which are all utterly delicious. Though they may be eaten raw, their flavor is enhanced by gentle cooking.

To Prepare Brush off any dirt and trim away the tough ends of the stems. Most chanterelles are delightful sautéed with garlic and shallots, or served with delicious creamy sauces, mixed into pasta, or with chicken, meat, or fish. I especially like black chanterelles and trompette de la mort sautéed and served with salmon, or layered with potatoes for a rustic winter gratin.

Chinese Black Mushroom See Shiitake Mushroom
Chinese Black Fungus See Black Fungus
Cremini See Brown Mushroom

Trompettes de la mort

Chicken of the Forest, Chicken of the Woods

This large fungus, *Laetiporus sulphureus*, grows in woodlands from the base of oak, willow, wild cherry, and yew trees especially. It is huge and fan shaped, sometimes growing in grotesque, scary-looking layers. Its flesh is dense and fibrous; if it is too old it is very tough and dry as cotton or sawdust, and may taste slightly sour—not a pleasant culinary experience. When young enough to eat, however, it has a fine flavor and chickeny taste and texture. Although it is available commercially, it may take some hunting.

Easy Recipe

Exotic Mushroom-filled Enchiladas
Mix sautéed wild mushrooms with ricotta cheese and shredded Parmesan to taste. Roll up into soft flour or corn tortillas and arrange in an ovenproof-dish. Top with mild red chili enchilada sauce, a layer of shredded mild cheese, such as Jack or white Cheddar, and bake in a 400°F oven until the cheese melts and the dish is warmed through.

To Prepare Brush away any dirt and trim off any dry or discolored parts. Braise or sauté as other mushrooms. In addition, this fungus may be treated as you would chicken, to be sliced into cutlets, and browned in a little olive oil.

Cuitlacoche

This fungus grows on corn kernels, hidden from prying eyes under the outer husk. It is extremely ugly. Its swollen, purplish, cancerous-looking growths deform and then displace the little golden corn kernels. To the uninitiated it simply looks revolting. To the aficionado, it is known as the "truffle of Mexico" for the simple reason that it is wonderfully fragrant and tasty, and is mainly available in Mexico.

To Prepare Though seldom found fresh outside Mexico, cuitlacoche may be found canned or frozen occasionally. Sauté, then serve wrapped in warm, soft corn tortillas, with a spoonful of spicy, fresh salsa, and perhaps a little shredded mild cheese.

Cultivated, or Common, Mushroom

These are usually available in small (button), medium, or large sizes, the largest having opened and exposing their black gills, also known as large flat black mushrooms. Each size is best for a different purpose.

The small mushrooms are good for sautéeing; the medium ones for sautéeing, salads, and sauces. The largest ones, sometimes called portabellos, are stronger in flavor, a bit too inky for anything too delicate, but terrific drizzled with olive oil and garlic, a dash of lemon juice, or balsamic vinegar, and set out on the barbecue. Common cultivated mushrooms are readily and widely available throughout the year.

To Prepare Wipe the mushrooms with a damp cloth or paper towel, or soft brush. Since they are grown in sterilized soil, you do not need to wash them and, indeed, washing them will only make them sodden and soggy when cooked. They are good sautéed, stir-fried, simmered, or raw in salads. Flat black mushrooms are delicious roasted, sautéed, and any time you want a fuller mushroom flavor. Use with porcini-flavored stock cubes for a budget version of risotto alla porcini.

Button mushrooms

Large open mushrooms

Enoki

Enoki look like a cross between a long, tall white mushroom and a beansprout. They grow, in sterilized soil, in clumps. They are delicate and need no cooking. They are very tasty in sandwiches, as a garnish for sushi, and are also used in nouvelle cuisine, scattered over duck and kiwi salad, for example. Enoki are very good tossed at the last minute into soups and stir-fries, or in the filling of a pot sticker or spring roll. They are available fresh, usually vacuum packed.

Enoki are usually sold in oriental food shops and specialty grocers shops.

To Prepare Choose enoki that are white and firm, with no yellow discoloration or slimy edges. As they are grown in sterilized soil, they do not need to be cleaned, though the root cluster should be trimmed away. They are best raw in salads, or simmered in clear soup, or tossed into a stir-fry.

Enoki grow in clumps, are delicate, and don't need cooking.

Fairy Ring Champignon or Mushroom
(Marasmius oreades)

These small mushrooms grow in circles on pastures or lawns. They are excellent for all sorts of dishes, especially in omelets or pastas, or sautéed with chicken. In season—spring through winter—you may find them fresh, and they are available dried year round.

To Prepare To use fresh, brush off any dirt and trim the stem ends. To use dry, rehydrate as you would any other mushroom.

Field Mushrooms See Champignon.

Flat Black Mushroom, Flat Mushroom See Cultivated, or Common, Mushrooms.

Hedgehog Fungus

Also known as dentinums, hedgehog fungi have creamy white flesh that is best slowly cooked, when it tastes somewhat like chanterelles. Not often available in shops, you can occasionally find them fresh. They come in two sizes, one large, one smaller, and the cap varies from orange-brown to white, with a wide array of colors in between. They are very nice pan roasted with garlic and olive oil, or braised with meats or fish.

To Prepare Scrape off the spines on the underside of the cap; these give a bitter taste. Blanching tenderizes and takes off the bitter edge.

Easy Recipe

Roman Panino
(Italian for "roll" or "biscuit")
Sauté mushrooms of any sort in olive oil, and season with salt and chopped garlic. Halve a loaf of bread (preferably rosemary focaccio) horizontally, and press the mushrooms onto the bottom half. Cover with a thick slice of fresh mozzarella or mild soft goat cheese, and close up. Eat with a mid-afternoon glass of crisp, dry white wine.

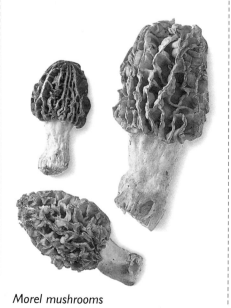

Morel mushrooms

Honey Fungus

Armillaria mellea is sometimes called boot-lace fungus, because of its appearance, and is called famigliole in Italy, since it grows in "little families" or clusters. It is edible when cooked, but is not eaten raw.

To Prepare The fungus should be blanched for 5 minutes as it is mildly toxic. After blanching, sauté in garlicky butter or olive oil, and serve with pasta, or add to soups and stews. The stems can be woody and tough, and should be discarded.

Horn of Plenty See Chanterelle

Horse Mushroom See Champignon

Monkey's Head Fungus

(also known as Lion's Mane)

This delicate white frilly specimen is very tasty indeed, though not easily found. It is sometimes sold under the name lion's head. When I first described a monkey's head fungus to someone, the only adjective that came to mind was "fluffy," a fluffy white mushroom.

This coral or sponge-like fungus is particularly good in plain meat or vegetable stock, oriental-style, or as part of a gentle sauté of mixed mushrooms. I think it adds delicious interest and texture to stir-frys.

To Prepare Soak in cold water several times for about 10 minutes each. This is because the many folds of the fungus are very attractive to tiny insects. Blanch the fungus for a minute, rinse in cold water, then add it at the last minute to your recipe.

Morel Mushroom

Known in French as morilles, these ruffle-topped wild mushrooms are unsurpassed for flavor. I will never forget my first taste: slightly smoky, distinctly foresty, they tasted like nothing else I had ever eaten.

Morels come in many varieties, each one absolutely delicious. They range in color from yellowish, through brown, through black. Sautéed, simmered, braised, or used in a sauce, they are superb to eat and to use to flavor other foods. Morels are one of those mushrooms, which, though both are wonderful, are almost better in their dried rather than fresh state, as the flavor is concentrated in the drying process.

To Prepare Brush or wipe the fresh morels with a damp paper towel, and trim the stem ends. Then cut them in half and brush any soil from the inside. Morels should always be cooked, as they can disagree with some people when eaten raw.

Mousseron

These tiny little caps on long thin stems are pale beige-brown in color. They have a fragrant porcini-like aroma and a similar, though milder, flavor.

Their small stature makes them seem jewel-like, a tiny treasure of the forest. Use them anywhere you would use porcini, or in conjunction with other mushrooms. You will find mousserons are as wonderful dried as they are fresh.

To Prepare Wipe with a damp cloth or paper towel if you can, though they are quite small to wipe individually. Mousserons are good sautéed in omelets, or with chicken.

Mousserons

Ovoli

Italian in origin, these mushrooms have a lovely scarlet-orange cap shaped like an oval, hence the nickname, ovoli. Their proper name is *Amanita caesarea*. They have a lovely pleasing flavor, are usually found fresh, and may be used instead of porcini.

They are at their best when very thinly sliced and eaten as a salad, with or without porcini, and if you have a truffle—white or black—to shave over it, oh-la-la!

To Prepare Wipe with a damp paper towel, and use as desired.

Easy Recipe

Mushroom Filling

Sauté any mushroom, or combination of mushrooms, and add to the egg-cream filling of a quiche or savory tart. Scatter with shredded cheese, and bake according to your recipe.

Oyster Mushroom

Named pleurotte in French and shemeji in Japanese, the smooth texture and sealike flavor of this mushroom are the only connections to fish that it has, despite its English name. The French name is perhaps more apt, as it derives from "pleurer" (to cry), referring to the way in which this mushroom soaks up water so readily.

Though it grows wild, the oyster mushroom is now cultivated commercially and comes in a variety of types: black, walnut, pink, yellow, and the more commonly found pale gray.

Oyster mushrooms can be sautéed, used in soups or sauces, barbecued, lightly sautéed then tossed into salads, or chopped and used in a wide variety of dishes.

I prefer oyster mushrooms fresh, though they are sold dried as well.

To Prepare Brush lightly and trim away the tough stem ends. Never wash in water as they act like sponges.

Oyster mushrooms

Pied Blu mushrooms

Parasol Mushroom

Macrolepiota procera, more commonly known as parasols, are slightly pointed umbrella-shaped mushrooms with a flavor similar to porcini. They are delicious used for stuffing, roasting, and broiling. Another parasol, the shaggy parasol, is less tasty, and can cause stomach upsets, though many people do eat it happily.

To Prepare Wipe the caps clean with a damp piece of kitchen paper or a clean kitchen towel. If using for stuffing, remove the stem and use the stem to make soup or a base for a sauce. If using the whole mushroom, trim the bottom of the stem end.

Pied Blu

These are a cultivated mushroom, predictably bland in flavor but with a surprising blue tinge that grows brighter as they cook. Use pied blu as you would any mild mushrooms, braised or sautéed, without adding other colors to distract from the unusual hue of the fungus. They look attractive surrounding braised or roasted meats, in a foresty, rustic way.

To Prepare Wipe the mushrooms with a damp cloth, trim the stems if using.

Porcini

The family *Boletus* includes a number of edible and utterly delicious mushrooms. They range in color from off-white to dark red, and are wonderful raw as well as cooked. The *Boletus edulis*, called cep in France (cèpe in French) and porcini in Italy, grows in lavish abundance on the Continent in the fall, and even in the summer if it has been wet enough. It is regarded as one of the joys of French and Italian cuisine. In this book the mushroom is referred to as "porcini."

Porcini are available both fresh and dried. The drying process concentrates the flavor and aroma, giving a deep taste to any dish in which porcini are used. Use with abandon and delight. Dried varieties come from France and Italy, but also from Argentina which exports a variety with an especially smoky flavor.

To Prepare Choose fresh porcini when they are firm, and check for insect life. Brush off any dirt and wipe with a damp paper towel. Do not wash or soak fresh porcini as they soak up water like a sponge and will disintegrate into a soupy mess. Trim the tough stem ends and discard. The stems themselves are edible and deliciously strong flavored. Make sure the spore-bearing body does not become too spongy when cooked. Porcini are wonderful sautéed, braised, stir-fried, or simmered.

Easy Recipe

Polenta Gratin with Sautéed Porcini and Cream

Sauté fresh or rehydrated porcini in a little butter with a few chopped shallots, then pour in enough light cream to make a rich sauce. Season with grated nutmeg, salt, and a little cayenne pepper. Layer with firm polenta, top with shredded Parmesan, and bake in a hot oven until heated through and golden brown on top.

Portobello

These are simply the ordinary flat black mushroom, grown to huge proportions. Portobellos are a popular choice for barbecuing or broiling. Serve on their own or alongside rare steak. Try serving barbecued portobellos sandwiched between the covers of a hamburger bun to vegetarians in lieu of a beefburger.

To Prepare Simply wipe with a damp paper towel to remove any earth or dirt. Marinating before barbecuing or broiling enhances its flavor delightfully. A scattering of chopped garlic, fresh herbs, olive oil, and lemon juice or balsamic vinegar is all you need.

Puff-Ball

This wild mushroom is seldom found in shops. It is a huge, smooth, round fungus which can reach over 40 pounds in weight, and because of this is sold in slices. Size, by the way, is no indication of maturity: sometimes they are large but young; at other times they may be small but past their prime.

To Prepare Trim the stem end, peel the skin, and slice the mushroom thinly. Puff-balls are very nice breaded and fried until crisp, or dice them and sauté or stir-fry. They are good with meats, too.

Saffron Milk Cap

Saffron milk caps, or *Lactarius deliciosus*, are salmon-colored mushrooms with a nutty, delicate flavor. They are not often available in shops; if they are, they will be fresh.

To Prepare Wipe with a damp cloth or paper towel and blanch to rid them of any bitterness before you cook according to your chosen recipe.

Shaggy Ink Cap

The *Coprinus comatus*, sometimes called lawyer's wig, are long, tall mushrooms of a pale whitish color on the outside, with an inky black pulp developing on the underside as they open and mature. They are good prepared as you would any other mushroom.

To Prepare The shaggy ink cap can be delicious, though it must be treated with care. Only the young firm mushrooms are worth eating, and should be prepared as soon as possible, as they deteriorate rapidly. Wipe the closed egg-shaped cups with a damp cloth to rid them of any sand, then cook. They don't need to be blanched if used immediately, but as they deteriorate so rapidly, blanch them if you need to keep them a few days.

Portobello mushrooms

Easy Recipe

Gnocchi with Wild Mushrooms
Sauté a handful of assorted wild mushrooms with salt, pepper, and chopped garlic. Toss with gnocchi, and serve with shaved or coarsely shredded Parmesan cheese, and a nugget of mascarpone cheese.

Shiitake Mushroom

Virtually the same type of mushroom as the Chinese black mushroom, they are 1–2½ inches in size, and vary in color from pale brownish to nearly black. They are available both fresh and dried, the former favored by the Japanese, while the latter is a staple of the Chinese kitchen. Shiitakes have a foresty flavor and hearty meaty texture. They are cultivated on oak or composite wood logs, and are delicious used in oriental recipes, but also complement Mediterranean and European cuisine, being especially good with olive oil. They are terrific barbecued.

Dried shiitakes are quite superb. Buy them in oriental food shops or from other sources who handle dried mushrooms.

To Prepare Brush or wipe the fresh ones clean and dry. Trim off their stems, before using. Soak or simmer the dried mushrooms until they are tender. Remove the stems if they are tough—oak-raised shiitake stems are usually edible; shiitake stems raised on composite material are tough.

Straw Mushroom

These Chinese mushrooms are oval in shape with a tight-fitting cap and slightly grayish hue. They are usually available only in cans.

To Prepare Drain the canned mushrooms and add them to most any stir-fry.

Trompette de la Mort See Chanterelle.

Truffle

Truffles grow beneath the surface of the earth and must be hunted by either a pig or dog, if you are in France, or a dog if you are in Italy. Truffles may be black such as the Périgord truffle or *Tuber melanosporum* or they may be the white fragrant *Tuber magnatum*. There is another, the summer truffle, *Tuber aestivum* which can be found in England, and while pleasant is not quite as exciting. Truffles can be found in other parts of the world, such as in the Arabian desert, but they are flavorless.

Black truffles are eaten either cooked or raw, often paired with or included in pâtés and chicken dishes, while Italy's white truffle is often shaved onto pasta or risotto, or buttery scrambled eggs.

To Prepare Because truffles are extremely expensive care must be taken in their preparation so as not to waste any of the precious flavor and aroma.

When you buy a truffle, make sure it is firm and heavy, and that if there are any holes made by insects, they haven't been filled up with dirt to make the truffle heavier on the scales.

Truffles can be cooked with food, but one of the best ways to

Shiitake mushrooms

Easy Recipe

Stuffed Shiitake Mushrooms
Uses shiitake caps to fill with a sui mai (Chinese steamed pork, turkey, or tofu dumpling) type of filling. Steam and serve with a dipping sauce of soy sauce and sesame oil.

appreciate their distinctive perfume is to shave them using a mandolino. The very thin shavings of truffle are dispersed throughout the dish and are very good with pasta, risotto, or salads.

White truffles are very delicate and keep only up to 7 days. Do not wash white truffles, simply brush them with a little suede brush. Wrap the cleaned truffles in tissue paper in a tightly closed plastic box and keep them in the refrigerator. Black truffles need to be brushed quite heartily or even washed and scrubbed, as the wartier skin easily traps earth. They will keep up to 14 days if similarly wrapped.

Wood Blewitt

A creamy gray mushroom with a startling violet-color tinge, especially evident on its stem. Available wild or cultivated, they have a mild flavour and firm texture, and are good with both East and West cuisines.
To Prepare Wipe with damp cloth, then cook as desired – I like them sliced and sautéed with lots of garlic.

Mushroom Products

Butters Truffle and/or porcini butter is usually sold in one-ounce jars. The butter provides pure flavor. Rub it underneath the skin of a chicken before roasting, or spread it onto hot, toasted pain levain.

Crumbled Dried Mushrooms Porcini or morels are available as a powder that can be used for sprinkling over dishes at the last minute, such as risotti.

Mushroom Soy Sauce This is simply soy sauce that is infused with the flavor of mushroom.

Porcini and/or Truffle Condiments Also known by their Italian name, condimenti, the fragrant pastes of truffle, porcini, or truffle and porcini are quite sublime and can transform anything they are spooned onto.

Porcini Oil This is oil that is flavored with the essence of porcini mushrooms. Use it to drizzle onto greens or over broiled chicken or fish, or to finish a dish of sautéed mushrooms.

Preserved Mushrooms and Fungi Sold in a jar, preserved mushrooms are first simmered in seasoned vinegar redolent of cloves and herbs, then submerged under a layer of olive oil.

Stock Cubes These are available with the strong flavor of porcini mushrooms. Their stock makes a great base for risotto or soup, or sauce for any sort of meat or pasta, to be fleshed out with a handful of the real thing.

Easy Recipe

Ramen-type Noodle Soup with Shiitake Mushrooms

Rehydrate a handful of shiitakes in the stock from ramen-type noodles. Season with a little garlic, soy sauce, and sesame oil, if desired, and serve with snipped chives or garlic chives scattered over.

Dried mushrooms

Introduction

Dried Mushrooms

Generally speaking, you will need to seek out specialty shops when you require certain dried fungi, although dried porcini are increasingly available in supermarkets.

Rehydrating Dried Mushrooms Pour hot water over the mushrooms, cover, and leave to soak for about 20 minutes. Alternatively, place the mushrooms in a saucepan, cover with cold water, and bring to a boil. Reduce the heat, and simmer for 5 minutes. Then cover and leave to plump up, about 10 minutes more.

Straining Mushroom Soaking Liquid Most mushrooms contain some grit and, when they are rehydrated, this is transferred to the soaking liquid. (Some mushrooms may require a second soaking in cold water.) This liquid is full of flavor and is invaluable in cooking. (It is referred to as "mushroom liquid" in this book.)

The liquid must be strained before use. Either use a coffee filter paper, or pour the liquid through a wire strainer lined with a piece of cheesecloth. Alternatively, since the grit settles at the bottom of the container, you can usually pour off the clear mushroom liquid leaving a little at the bottom to discard with the grit.

Adding Dried Mushrooms Directly to a Recipe Dried mushrooms can be used in place of fresh ones, though the flavors are slightly different. Since dried mushrooms are concentrated in flavor, they are sometimes preferable to fresh. If you need volume, combine them with cultivated mushrooms.

The most common way of adding dried mushrooms to a recipe is to rehydrate them. You can also add them directly to the pan, if there is sufficient liquid in the dish for them to absorb. Italian tomato or wine sauces and stews, or hearty soups are all fine to add the dried mushrooms straight into. Take care, however, that your mushrooms are not too sandy—if they are you will have grit at the bottom of the pan. If you suspect your mushrooms of this, rehydrate them before using them in the recipe.

Making the Most of Stems

Any stems trimmed while you are preparing mushroom caps should be used for soups, stocks, and sauces. Not only is it economical, but the stems have concentrated flavors, and since their flesh is often fibrous and tough, they take well to a long, strong, boiling.

Mushrooms make marvelous appetizers as they are light yet flavorful. The simplest things, such as grilled or sautéed mushrooms eaten over crisp crostini, start a meal delightfully.

See other chapters, covering soups, vegetables, and pizzas and snacks, to find many many mushroomy dishes that are ideal appetizers. Dishes like Crisp-fried Mushroom Patties (see page 28), or Bags of Mushrooms, (see page 32), are terrific to dig into before you go on to any other course.

antipasti and appetizers

Roasted Portobellos

with Pink Peppercorns, Chervil, and Pine Nuts

This dish is easy to prepare yet is strikingly delicious. You may use large flat black mushrooms in place of portobellos if you like. If you do not have chervil to sprinkle over them, use fresh tarragon; and if you do not have fresh tarragon, use chopped parsley and snipped chives.

SERVES 4

- 4 portobello mushrooms or 12 large flat black mushrooms
- 5 cloves garlic, chopped
- 4–6 Tbsp extra virgin olive oil, or as desired
- 2 Tbsp balsamic vinegar
- salt, to taste
- 4 Tbsp pine nuts
- 1–2 tsp pink peppercorns, or as desired
- 1 Tbsp fresh chervil, chopped

Preparation: 40 minutes
Cooking time : 15 minutes

❶ Arrange the mushrooms in a broiler pan or on a baking sheet, and sprinkle with the garlic, olive oil, balsamic vinegar, and salt. Leave to marinate for 30 minutes.

❷ Meanwhile, lightly toast the pine nuts in a heavy-based, ungreased frying pan, over medium-high heat, tossing every few moments, until the pine nuts are golden and lightly browned in spots. Remove from the heat and set aside.

❸ Broil the mushrooms in their marinade, or bake in a 400°F oven, until they are browned on their gill sides. Then turn them over and cook until the outsides are lightly browned, or the mushrooms are just tender, about 10–15 minutes.

❹ Arrange the mushrooms on individual plates, with any juices spooned over, and scatter over the pine nuts, pink peppercorns, and chervil. Serve immediately.

antipasti and appetizers

Mixed Mushroom and Black Olive Tapenade

Tapenade aux Champignons *This flavorful spread is delicious heaped onto crisp, thin little toasts, or spread onto crusty baguettes for a heartier bite. Add some cream cheese on top or melt some fresh mozzarella cheese, using focaccio as the base and eat with a roll of bread. The tapenade is also good used as a relish with anything barbecued.*

Take care to sauté the onion gently and slowly, rather than quickly browning it. Then, after adding the mushrooms, ensure that they, too, cook slowly, developing their rich flavor and losing any watery quality.

SERVES 4

- 1 onion, chopped
- 3–4 Tbsp olive oil
- 3 ripe fresh tomatoes, shredded (discard the skins left behind)
- 8 oz fresh cultivated common mushrooms, finely chopped
- ½–1 oz mixed dried mushrooms, such as trompettes de la mort, mousserons, morel mushrooms, porcini and chanterelles, broken into pieces (or use 1 lb mixed fresh mushrooms, and omit the dried)
- 1–2 sprigs fresh thyme
- 2–3 garlic cloves, chopped
- 20–25 black oil-cured olives, pitted and chopped
- ground black pepper, to taste

Preparation: 10 minutes
Cooking time : 30 minutes

❶ Very gently lightly sauté the onion in the olive oil until softened and golden brown, about 10–15 minutes. When the onion is softened, add the tomato, and continue cooking until the tomato "melts" and the mixture becomes pastelike. The oil should have separated from the onion.

❷ Add the fresh and dried mushrooms, if using, and the thyme, and cook gently for about 20 minutes, stirring and turning occasionally, until the mushrooms are very soft and tender. If the mixture becomes too dry, add some stock or dry white wine.

❸ When the mixture has thickened, remove from the heat, and stir in the garlic and the olives. Mix well and season with pepper. Let cool to room temperature.

Mixed Antipasto of Meats, Vegetables,
and Preserved Mushrooms

Antipasto Misto con Funghi *This delicious appetizer is not only easy to throw together, it is a good excuse for a rummage through your favorite Italian or other Mediterranean deli. When fresh porcini or other succulent mushrooms are available, I slice one or two up and add them to the platter. If you are feeling extravagant, drizzle truffle oil over them as well.*

SERVES 4

- 12–16 Tbsp mixed oil-cured mushrooms
- 4 slices each Italian salami, smoked turkey or goose breast, bresaola or prosciutto
- 8 marinated artichoke hearts
- 25–30 oil-cured black olives
- 5–10 Tbsp oil-cured roasted red sweet peppers
- arugula leaves, to garnish
- a drizzle of truffle oil and a fresh porcini mushroom, thinly sliced, to garnish (optional)

Preparation: 10 minutes
Cooking time : 15 minutes

❶ Arrange the ingredients on a large serving platter. Serve with plenty of crusty country bread and sweet butter. Your guests should help themselves.

Pot Stickers of Many Mushrooms

and Smoked Tofu

Meaty mushrooms make a delicious filling for all sorts of Chinese dumplings, especially vegetarian ones such as the following. It makes a good mixture for won tons, too, or add a handful of beansprouts for a crisp spring-roll filling.

SERVES 4
- ½ oz cellophane noodles
- 3–4 Tbsp tree cloud fungus
- 6–8 Chinese black mushrooms
- 3½ oz enoki mushrooms, cut into bite-size pieces
- 5–6 oz smoked tofu, diced, roughly chopped, or shredded
- 3 scallions, thinly sliced
- 1 small carrot, finely chopped
- 3 garlic cloves, chopped
- 2 tsp sesame oil
- 1 Tbsp chopped fresh ginger root
- 1 Tbsp soy sauce
- 1 Tbsp chopped fresh cilantro
- gyoza wrappers
- oil, for frying
- hot pepper oil or chili-garlic paste, white wine vinegar, and soy sauce, to serve

Preparation: 40 minutes

Cooking time : 10 minutes

❶ Cook the noodles according to the instructions on the package. Then drain, cut into bite-size lengths, and set aside.

❷ Place the tree cloud fungus and black mushrooms in a saucepan and cover with water. Bring to a boil, then remove from the heat, and let stand for 15 minutes, or until both the mushrooms and fungus are soft. Remove the mushrooms and fungus from the water. Trim the stems of the mushrooms and cut into fine julienne strips. Trim the tough ends of the tree cloud fungus, then cut into shreds.

❸ Combine the cellophane noodles with the rehydrated mushrooms and tree cloud fungus, the enoki, tofu, scallions, carrot, garlic, sesame oil, ginger, soy sauce, and cilantro.

❹ Fill each gyoza wrapper with a spoonful of the mixture and fold over, moistening the edges of the wrappers so that they stick. (Traditional pot stickers are made with a slightly different dough, and they are pleated on each side for a plumper dumpling. Pleat if you can.)

❺ To cook, heat a wok or heavy-based frying pan until smoking, then add about ½ cup water and 3 tablespoons vegetable oil. Add the dumplings, cover, and cook for about 2 minutes. Then remove the lid and let the liquid evaporate. Now fry the dumplings until golden and crisp, 1– 2 minutes.

❻ Remove the pot stickers from the pan. Serve immediately, with hot pepper oil or chili-garlic paste, a cruet of vinegar, and one of soy sauce, letting each diner make his or her own dipping sauce.

TIP:

Strain the mushroom liquid to use for soups. It can be frozen if it is not required straight away.

antipasti and appetizers

Crisp-fried Mushroom Patties

Croquettas de Setas *Crisp crumb-coated croquettes of mixed wild and tamed mushrooms bound with a thick béchamel sauce, egg yolk, and a little shredded Parmesan, this Spanish dish is delicious served as an appetizer or a tapa with a wedge of lemon if you like, or on a plate with a few leaves of arugula.*

SERVES 4

- 2 Tbsp butter
- 2 Tbsp flour
- 1 cup hot, but not boiling, milk
- a grating of nutmeg
- salt and ground black pepper, to taste
- 12 oz fresh mushrooms, sliced or roughly chopped
- 1 egg yolk
- 4–6 Tbsp shredded Parmesan cheese
- 3 scallions, chopped
- 3 garlic cloves, chopped
- 2 pinches dried thyme
- 1 cup dried bread crumbs, for dredging
- vegetable oil, for frying
- lemon wedges, to serve

Preparation: 30 minutes
Cooking time : 15 minutes

❶ Melt the butter in a saucepan, then sprinkle with flour, and cook a few minutes, until light golden but not brown. Off the heat, stir in the milk, nutmeg, salt, and pepper. Stir with a wooden spoon until slightly thickened. Return to the heat and cook, stirring, until thickened. Then boil gently for about 5 minutes.

❷ Remove from the heat, let cool, then pour the sauce into a bowl, and chill for at least 2 hours.

❸ Combine the chilled sauce with the mushrooms, egg yolk, Parmesan cheese, scallions, garlic, and thyme. Place 2–3 tablespoons of the mixture into the bread crumbs and roll, patting it until the crumbs stick. Continue until all the mixture is used up. Place the patties on a plate in the fridge to firm up.

❹ Heat the oil in a saucepan, to a depth of about 1–2 inches, until it just smokes.

❺ Gently ease each patty into the hot oil, taking care not to splash yourself, and cook until browned on the first side. Then turn them over and cook on the second side until golden brown. These are best when crunchy on the outside, and creamy within. Do not turn them too soon, or they will fall apart. Croquettas also cook well in a deep-fat fryer.

❻ Serve warm with lemon wedges for squeezing over.

Crostini of Rosemary Polenta

Crostini de Polenta con Funghi *Little squares of rosemary- and parsley-flecked polenta are spread with a thin layer of rich, truffled pâté, all topped with thinly sliced raw mushrooms. Try raw porcini, or raw shiitakes are tasty too. The important thing is that the mushrooms are sliced very thinly so that they fall in a light pile on top of each little morsel; also this somehow enhances the flavor of the mushroom.*

SERVES 4

- 1 cup water
- a pinch of salt
- 4 slightly heaping tablespoons instant polenta
- 2 tsp chopped fresh parsley
- 1 tsp chopped fresh rosemary
- olive oil, for greasing
- 1–2 raw, firm fresh porcini
- 3–4 oz rich pâté, truffled if possible, or several tablespoons truffle/porcini condiment mixed with an equal amount of softened butter

Preparation: 40 minutes

Cooking time : 10 minutes

❶ Place the water in a saucepan and bring to a boil. Add the salt, then stir in the polenta, and cook over medium heat, stirring with a wooden spoon, until thickened, about 5 minutes. Stir in the parsley and rosemary.

❷ Grease a small cake pan (about 6–8 inches) and spoon the polenta into it. Leave to cool, or chill in the fridge for about 30 minutes.

❸ Slice the mushrooms very, very thinly.

❹ Cut the firm polenta into bite-size squares, and spread each with a bit of the pâté or condiment/butter mix. Top with the sliced mushroom. Serve immediately.

Spinach-stuffed Mushrooms

Funghi Ripieni *I have never subscribed to the view that life is too short to stuff a mushroom. A stuffed mushroom, roasting in the oven, its juices mingling with its savory filling, is a delightful proposition.*

SERVES 4

- 1 lb firm, cultivated, open-cup mushrooms
- 3–5 Tbsp butter or olive oil
- 3–5 garlic cloves, roughly chopped
- 6 oz cooked, chopped spinach
- 3–5 scallions, thinly sliced
- 2–3 tsp fresh marjoram, basil, thyme, and/or rosemary
- 3 oz freshly shredded Parmesan or pecorino cheese, plus a little extra for sprinkling
- 1 egg, lightly beaten
- bread crumbs, for binding
- salt and ground black pepper, to taste

Preparation: 20-30 minutes

Cooking time : 20 minutes

❶ Preheat a 375°F oven. Break the stems off of all the mushrooms and chop finely. In the butter or oil, lightly sauté the mushroom stems with the garlic, then add the spinach, scallions, and fresh herbs. Remove from the heat and mix in the remaining ingredients, using just enough bread crumbs to hold the mixture together. If the filling doesn't seem mushroomy enough, take a few of the mushroom caps, chop them finely, then add them to the filling.

❷ Arrange the caps on a baking sheet and fill each one with the filling, pressing it in firmly. Sprinkle with cheese, then bake for 10–15 minutes, or until the mushrooms are juicy and the cheese lightly browned. Serve immediately.

VARIATION:

Add a teaspoonful or two of pesto to this dish, or a bit of either chopped prosciutto or diced browned Italian sausage.

Shiitake Mushrooms with Smoked Tofu,

Spring Greens, and Soy-sesame Dressing

Smoked poultry—such as chicken, turkey, or duck—may be used in place of the tofu, or omit altogether and serve the shiitakes with the greens.

Sometimes I include a cruet filled with hot chili oil and another with rice vinegar to add in droplets to the dipping sauce, as the whim of the diner takes him or her.

SERVES 4

- 10–15 dried shiitake or Chinese black mushrooms, or 8–10 large ones, halved once rehydrated
- 1 or 2 heads of spring greens
- 12 oz smoked tofu, cut into bite-size pieces
- 2–3 Tbsp sesame oil, or as desired
- $\frac{1}{4}$–$\frac{1}{2}$ tsp soy sauce

Preparation: 15-20 minutes

Cooking time : 15-20 minutes

❶ Place the shiitake or black mushrooms in a saucepan and cover with cold water. Bring to a boil, reduce the heat, and simmer for 10 minutes, or until tender. Cover while you prepare the greens.

❷ Discard any large or tough leaves from the spring greens, then trim the tough stalk ends. Blanch the leaves in boiling water for a minute or so, until they turn bright green, then take the leaves and plunge them into very cold water. You may need to do this in several batches.

❸ When the shiitake or black mushrooms are cool enough to handle, remove them from the saucepan, and squeeze them tightly. Cut off the tough stems and discard.

❹ Roll the spring greens tightly together and, with a sharp knife, cut into fine shreds.

❺ Arrange the greens on a serving plate along with the mushrooms and tofu. On a separate small plate, pour the sesame oil, then drizzle in the soy sauce. Serve this with the vegetables and let each person dip a mushroom, some greens, or piece of tofu into the soy-sesame dressing as they eat.

TIP:

If spring greens are not available, use young cabbage, mustard greens, or bok choy.

antipasti and appetizers

Bags of Mushrooms

Crispy filo pastry packages, the paper-thin dough twirled to form a fanlike top, contain several mouthfuls of delicious filling, giving a variety of tastes and textures.

SERVES 6–8

- 5 shallots, or ½ onion, chopped
- 3 garlic cloves, chopped
- 1–2 Tbsp olive oil or butter
- 8 oz mixed fresh mushrooms, thinly sliced
- ½ cup dry white wine
- ½ cup stock
- 2–3 Tbsp port
- 2 tsp cornstarch
- 5 Tbsp cold water
- 4–5 heaping tablespoons crème fraîche
- sea salt and ground black pepper, to taste
- a grating of nutmeg
- 2 tsp fresh tarragon, roughly chopped
- 6 sheets filo pastry
- olive oil or melted butter, for brushing

Preparation: 1 hour

Cooking time : 30-40 minutes

❶ Preheat a 400°F oven. Sauté the shallots or onion with the garlic in the olive oil or butter until softened, then add the fresh mushrooms, and sauté until lightly browned and tender.

❷ Pour in the wine and cook over high heat until the liquid is nearly evaporated. Add the stock and port, and cook over high heat until it also reduces to a thin sauce.

❸ Combine the cornstarch with the water and stir it into the sauce, along with the crème fraîche, salt and pepper, nutmeg, and tarragon. Simmer over medium-low heat for 5 minutes, or until thickened. Leave to cool, then taste for seasoning.

❹ To assemble the pastries, lay a sheet of filo pastry on a flat surface, brush with the olive oil or butter, then cover with a second sheet to form a double layer. Cut this into four equal squares.

❺ Into the center of each square place a heaping tablespoon or two of the filling, then gather the four corners together in the center, pressing tightly and neatly with your fingers to seal. Lift onto a baking sheet with a metal spatula.

❻ Bake for 15–20 minutes until golden and crisp, and serve immediately.

antipasti and appetizers

The flavor of mushrooms is released by simmering in liquid. Just a few mushrooms can add great flavor to soup, and in the winter a handful of dried mushrooms can have a magical effect. Dried mushrooms, especially, are delicious with so many of the ingredients we enjoy in soup. They complement white beans, potatoes, barley, and wild rice equally well.

And on its own, cooked only with well-chosen seasoning, a soup of mushrooms can be a truly delightful experience.

soups

Woodsey Soup of Turkey, Wild Rice, and Porcini

Minestra alla Bosca *This soup is good prepared with any sort of gamey meat, such as pheasant, or pork.*

SERVES 4–6

- 10 oz dark turkey meat, cut into bite-size pieces
- 1 onion, chopped
- ½ carrot, diced
- 1 bay leaf
- 3 Tbsp extra virgin olive oil
- 1 Tbsp flour
- 6 oz wild rice
- 2 potatoes, peeled and diced
- 5 cups chicken, game, or vegetable stock
- 1 oz dried mushrooms, such as porcini
- 8 oz common cultivated mushrooms, thinly sliced
- ¼ cup dry sherry, Madeira, or Marsala
- salt and ground black pepper, to taste

Preparation: 50 minutes

Cooking time : 1 hour

❶ Sauté the turkey with the onion, carrot, and bay leaf in 1 tablespoon of the olive oil until the onion is softened and the turkey lightly browned. Sprinkle in the flour and stir well to cook the flour through.

❷ Add the wild rice, potatoes, and stock, and bring to a boil. Reduce the heat to a simmer and cook over low heat until the rice is nearly tender, about 45 minutes.

❸ Meanwhile, rehydrate the mushrooms by pouring 1 cup hot, but not boiling, water over the mushrooms in a heatproof bowl. Cover and leave for about 30 minutes, then remove the mushrooms from the liquid and squeeze well over the bowl. Strain the soaking liquid and set aside.

❹ Sauté the sliced fresh mushrooms in the remaining olive oil, then add the rehydrated mushrooms, and cook together for a few minutes until the fresh mushrooms are lightly browned.

❺ Add the mushrooms to the soup mixture, along with the strained mushroom liquid. Pour in the sherry, Madeira, or Marsala, and season to taste. Serve immediately.

Tranquility Broth of Many Mushrooms

SERVES 4–6

- 5 dried shiitake or Chinese black mushrooms
- 2 Tbsp dried Chinese black fungus (tree cloud or cloud ears)
- 3 cups hot, but not boiling, water
- 1 onion, finely chopped
- 2 garlic cloves, chopped
- 3 cups chicken or vegetable stock
- 5–7 thin slices of fresh ginger root
- 8 oz mixed fresh mushrooms, such as shiitake mushrooms, enoki, chanterelles, button, straw, and curly white fungus
- 2 oz smoked tofu or smoked chicken breast, diced (optional)
- soy sauce, to taste

This light and gentle mushroom broth gets its flavor from its wide assortment of mushrooms, both fresh and dried.

Preparation: 45 minutes

Cooking time : 20-30 minutes

❶ Rehydrate the shiitake or Chinese black mushrooms and black fungus in the hot water. Let stand for 30 minutes, or until softened. Remove from the water and squeeze over the pan.

❷ Trim the hard bits and stem ends from the shiitake or Chinese black mushrooms and black fungus, and cut them into small strips. Strain the mushroom liquid. Return the trimmed and sliced shiitake or Chinese black mushrooms and black fungus to the strained liquid and set aside.

❸ Combine the onion, garlic, stock, and ginger in a pan. Bring to a boil, reduce the heat, and simmer gently for about 10 minutes.

❹ Add the mushroom liquid, rehydrated and fresh mushrooms to the soup. Simmer gently until the various mushrooms are cooked through, about 5–8 minutes.

❺ Add the diced, smoked tofu or chicken, if using, and season with soy sauce. Serve immediately.

Monkey's Head Fungus, Chicken, and Pea Soup

SERVES 4

- 1 monkey's head fungus, soaked and blanched (see page 15)
- 1 chicken breast, skinned and boned
- 5 cups fresh chicken stock
- 3–4 Tbsp baby petits pois, fresh or frozen
- salt and ground black pepper, to taste
- a pinch of nutmeg
- shredded Parmesan cheese, to serve (optional)

The unusual quality of this frilly, fluffy mushroom demands a clear bouillon so that it may be seen and admired. Since the stock is such an important part of the dish, I recommend that you use a homemade or fresh, storebought one rather than mix up a stock cube.

I added the strands of chicken for texture contrast, and the peas for the sheer beauty of their little dots of green.

Preparation: 5-10 minutes

Cooking time : 10 minutes

❶ Cut the monkey's head fungus into bite-size pieces and the chicken breast into fine strips. Place the fungus, chicken strips, and chicken stock in a saucepan. Bring to a boil, then add the peas, salt and pepper, and nutmeg. Bring to a boil again, to heat the peas through.

❷ Serve immediately, with Parmesan scattered over, if desired.

Creamy Rustic Purée of White Beans and Porcini

Potage aux Haricots et Porcini *Humble beans puréed with luxurious wild mushrooms create a classic soup throughout France's southwest. There is usually a scattering of shredded ham, such as prosciutto, and sometimes a shaving of truffle, a drizzle of truffle oil, or a scattering of diced creamy foie gras. Though the last ingredients aren't called for in the recipe, since the soup is lovely without them, if you happen to have any of them on hand, add them too, and feel decadent.*

SERVES 4–6

- 2½ cups cooked white beans, such as cannellini or lingots
- 10 cups stock, preferably ham
- ⅓ cup diced ham or bacon, such as pancetta or prosciutto
- 1 carrot, diced
- 1 baking potato, diced
- 2–3 tsp fresh thyme leaves
- 5 garlic cloves, roughly chopped
- 2 oz dried mushrooms such as porcini
- 1 cup water
- 3 Tbsp brandy
- salt and ground black pepper, to taste
- 2 Tbsp sweet butter or 3 Tbsp heavy cream

Preparation: 15-20 minutes

Cooking time :

45 minutes-1hour

❶ In a saucepan, combine the beans with the stock, ham or bacon, carrot, potato, half the thyme, and the garlic. Bring to a boil, then reduce the heat to low, and simmer until the vegetables are very tender and cooked through, about 30 minutes.

❷ Meanwhile, place the mushrooms with the water and brandy in a saucepan. Gradually bring to a boil, then reduce the heat, and simmer until the mushrooms are tender, about 15 minutes.

❸ Remove the mushrooms from the liquid, chop roughly, and add to the soup. Then strain the liquid, discarding the gritty bits, and add the strained liquid to the soup.

❹ Whiz the soup in the blender or food processor until smooth. Taste for seasoning, then stir in the butter or cream. Serve immediately in warmed bowls, garnished with the reserved thyme.

Miso Soup with Shiitake Mushrooms,

Buckwheat Soba, and Tofu

SERVES 4

- 6 dried shiitake or Chinese black mushrooms
- 2 cups water
- 4 oz buckwheat soba or thin noodles
- 2 cups chicken or vegetable stock
- ½ carrot, cut into thin julienne strips
- 1 Tbsp finely chopped Italian parsley
- 5 scallions, thinly sliced
- 4–5 oz tofu, cut into small pieces
- 2 Tbsp medium (brown) miso
- 1 Tbsp dark soy sauce
- 1 garlic clove, finely chopped
- ½ tsp sesame oil, or as desired
- a pinch of cayenne pepper or a few drops of hot pepper oil

This healthy, nourishing soup will start off a Japanese-style meal well, or would make a good lunch on its own.

Miso is made from fermented soy beans, and contains all their health-giving properties, though it is quite salty.

Preparation: 30 minutes

Cooking time : 15 minutes

❶ Place the shiitake or Chinese black mushrooms in a saucepan with the water, and bring to a boil. Reduce the heat and simmer for about 5 minutes, then remove from the heat and let cool. Squeeze out the mushrooms, cut off their tough stems, then slice into strips. Strain the mushroom liquid.

❷ Cook the buckwheat soba or noodles according to the instructions on the package. Drain and rinse with cold water.

❸ Place the mushroom liquid, stock, carrot, parsley, and half the scallions in a saucepan. Bring to a boil, then cook over medium heat for about 10 minutes. Add the tofu and warm through.

❹ Mix the miso with the soy sauce and garlic. Remove the soup from the heat, stir in the miso mixture, then add the soba or noodles and garlic. Serve each bowlful with a drizzle of sesame oil and a pinch of cayenne or hot pepper oil.

Mushroom Soup

Soupe aux Champignons *If you don't have the time or inclination to prepare toasted bread and cheese to accompany this soup, simply add a generous sprinkling of Parmesan cheese.*

SERVES 4

- 1 large onion, roughly chopped
- 6 Tbsp olive oil
- 4 garlic cloves, roughly chopped
- 4 fresh or canned tomatoes, shredded and skins discarded
- 8 oz common cultivated mushrooms, diced or sliced

- ½ oz mixed dried mushrooms, broken into small pieces or lightly crushed
- salt and ground black pepper, to taste
- 6¼ cups stock
- 2–3 sprigs thyme
- 4 or 8 slices of baguette or

- other crusty country bread
- 6–8 oz cheese, such as Gruyère, comte, Emmentaler, fontina, Jack, or asiago, thinly sliced
- ¼–⅓ cup dry sherry
- shredded Parmesan or pecorino cheese (optional)

soups

▲ *Mushroom Soup*

❶ Gently sauté the onion in the olive oil for about 20 minutes, stirring and shaking occasionally, until soft, golden, and lightly browned in places.

❷ Add the garlic, stir, and cook a few moments more. Then add the tomatoes and increase the heat slightly, until the tomatoes and onions form a reddish-colored paste-like mixture.

❸ Add the fresh and dried mushrooms. Sprinkle with salt and pepper, and continue to cook for about 20 minutes. The moisture from the fresh mushrooms will rehydrate the dried ones. If the mixture seems too dry, add a little dry white wine or stock.

❹ After this time, add the stock and thyme, and bring to a boil. Reduce the heat and simmer for 15–20 minutes more.

❺ To make the croûtes, place the bread on a baking sheet. Then put in a 400°F oven or under the broiler until it is dry and light golden. Turn the bread over and cook the other side. Remove from the oven or broiler, then top each with a slice of cheese, and a sprinkling of Parmesan or pecorino cheese, if using. Return to the oven or broiler until the cheese melts.

❻ Pour the sherry into the soup, and let it simmer in order to release its alcohol. Serve the soup ladled over the cheese-topped croûtes, with an extra sprinkling of Parmesan, if desired.

soups

39

Polish Mushroom and Barley Soup

with Celery Root

Krupnik *A big bowl of steaming mushroom barley soup is great when it's really cold, during a blizzard in New York City or a winter in Poland both of which places are home to the following soup. I like to eat it accompanied by thick slices of seeded rye bread, spread with sweet butter, and topped with a scallion.*

When, long ago, I ate it in Ratners, a dairy restaurant in New York's Lower East Side, and I asked about the soup, the owner took me aside and said: "Here is my secret; always a celery root." He liked me!

SERVES 4–6

- 1 carrot, sliced
- 1 onion, chopped
- 1 leek, chopped
- 2–3 Tbsp butter
- 1½–2 cups barley
- ½ oz mixed dried mushrooms
- 6¼–8 cups stock
- 3 garlic cloves, cut into chunks (optional)
- ¼–½ celery root, peeled and diced
- 2–3 bay leaves
- 1 large potato, diced
- salt and ground black pepper, to taste
- chopped fresh parsley, to serve

Preparation: 15 minutes

Cooking time : 1 hour

❶ Lightly sauté the carrot, onion, and leek in the butter until softened, about 5–10 minutes. Add the barley, mushrooms, stock, garlic, if using, celery root, and bay leaves. Bring to a boil, reduce the heat, and simmer until the barley is half tender, about 20 minutes.

❷ Add the potato, and continue to cook until the potato and barley are very tender. If the soup is too thick, add more stock; if it is too thin, boil it down to reduce a little.

❸ Test for seasoning and serve with parsley scattered over.

TIP:

If you want a deeper flavor, use chicken or goose fat in place of the butter. For a healthier option, use vegetable oil.

soups

41

Creamy Mushroom Soup with a Puff-pastry Top

Potage aux Champignons en Croûte This elegant soup is far simpler to prepare than it looks. The rich mushroom soup is ladled into ovenproof bowls and topped with puff pastry. Then it is popped into the oven and, as it bakes, the steam of the hot soup helps the pastry puff magnificently, forming a glorious topping. Dig into this crisp crust and free the fragrant mushroom steam, then enjoy them both together.

SERVES 4

- 3 oz each fresh oyster mushrooms (gray, yellow or pink), cultivated white mushrooms, and chanterelles or shiitakes, cut into ¼-inch slices
- 3 shallots, chopped
- 2 garlic cloves, chopped
- 3 Tbsp butter
- salt and ground black pepper, to taste
- 1 Tbsp flour
- 5 cups vegetable or other stock
- a few slices of dried mushrooms, such as porcini or trompette de la mort, or 1 tablespoon truffle/porcini condiment (optional)
- a grating of nutmeg
- 1 bay leaf
- 1 cup light cream
- 1 7 oz package puff pastry

Preparation: 20-30 minutes
Cooking time : 1 hour

❶ Preheat a 375°F oven. Sauté the fresh mushrooms, shallots, and garlic in the butter in a heavy-based saucepan or frying pan, until the vegetables are lightly browned in spots.

❷ Season with salt and pepper, then sprinkle in the flour. Cook for a few moments, stirring, then add the stock, and dried mushrooms, if using. Add the nutmeg and bay leaf, and cook for 15–20 minutes, stirring occasionally.

❸ Discard the bay leaf and stir in the cream. Add the truffle/porcini condiment now, if using. Ladle the soup into individual ovenproof baking dishes or crocks, preferably with a lip on which to anchor the pastry.

❹ Roll out the pastry and cover each bowl, letting the pastry drape over the edge. Seal the edges with water.

❺ Bake in the oven until the pastry tops are puffed up and golden brown, about 15–20 minutes. (The center of the crust may remain quite pale.)

❻ Serve immediately, letting each person break through his or her pastry topping to release the steam and fragrance of the foresty soup.

TIP:

Including a few slices of dried mushrooms, such as porcini or trompettes de la mort, will really boost the foresty flavor of this soup. Truffle/porcini condiment is the luxurious alternative.

soups

Salads of mushrooms are delicious, varied, and extremely versatile. There are so many different types of mushrooms, and many of them can be eaten either raw or simply warmed through.

salads

Warm Salad of Sautéed Mushrooms,

Goat Cheese, and Asparagus

Salade Tiède aux Champignons, Chèvre, et Asperges *This is quintessential bistro fare. You could, if you liked, add a handful of shredded prosciutto and/or toasted hazelnuts to this simply prepared but delicious salad.*

SERVES 4

- 12 oz small thin asparagus, tough ends broken off
- 3 shallots, chopped
- 2 garlic cloves, chopped
- 4 Tbsp olive oil
- 7 oz mixed salad greens
- salt and ground black pepper, to taste
- 1 Tbsp tarragon mustard
- 1 Tbsp raspberry or red wine vinegar
- 4 oz goat cheese, crumbled or broken into small pieces
- 12 oz mixed fresh mushrooms, such as oyster, chanterelles, enoki, porcini, and button, cut into strips or bite-size pieces
- 1 Tbsp balsamic vinegar or red wine
- 12 Tbsp chopped fresh chervil
- 2 Tbsp snipped fresh chives or chopped fresh tarragon

Preparation: 15-20 minutes
Cooking time : 10 minutes

❶ Cook the asparagus in rapidly boiling salted water until just tender and bright green, about 3 minutes. Drain, submerge in very cold water (add a few ice cubes to the water) to keep its bright green color and crisp texture, then drain once again. Set the asparagus aside while you prepare the rest of the salad.

❷ Mix 1 tablespoon of the chopped shallots with half the garlic and 1–2 tablespoon olive oil. Toss this with the greens, along with salt and pepper to taste.

❸ Mix 1 tablespoon olive oil with the tarragon mustard and the raspberry or red wine vinegar; stir well to combine, then pour it over the greens and toss well. Arrange the asparagus and goat cheese over the top.

❹ Sauté the mushrooms over a medium-high heat, with the remaining shallots and garlic, in the remaining olive oil until lightly browned. Pour in the balsamic vinegar or red wine, season with salt and pepper, then pour this hot mixture over the salad. Serve immediately, with the herbs scattered over.

salads

Salad of Raw Mushrooms and Cheese

Salade aux Champignons et Fromage *This classic salad of France can be accompanied by seasonal vegetables. When asparagus is in season, a few cooked spears are delicious alongside the mushrooms and cheese. The same goes for green beans or tender, boiled new potatoes.*

SERVES 4

- 1 lb firm common cultivated mushrooms, thinly sliced
- 12 oz Gruyère, Jarlsberg, comte, or similar cheese, cut into thin julienne strips
- 1–2 tsp fresh thyme or savory, chopped
- 3 shallots, finely chopped
- 2 Tbsp chopped fresh parsley
- 1 Tbsp Dijon-type mustard
- 1–2 Tbsp lemon juice, balsamic, or white wine vinegar
- 4 Tbsp vegetable oil
- salt and ground black pepper, to taste
- 1 beet, cooked, peeled, and diced, or 2 ripe tomatoes, quartered
- a handful or two of arugula or other mixed baby salad greens
- 2 hard-cooked eggs, cut into wedges

Preparation: 30 minutes

Cooking time : 15 minutes

❶ Mix the mushrooms with the cheese, thyme or savory, shallots, and parsley.

❷ Combine the mustard with lemon juice or vinegar, oil, and salt

and pepper. Mix a few spoonfuls with the diced beets or tomato quarters.

❸ Mix the remaining dressing with the mushrooms and cheese, and mound it onto a plate. Then garnish with the beet or tomato, arugula or other mixed baby salad greens, and the egg wedges.

❹ Serve immediately to avoid wilting salad greens and discolored eggs.

TIP:

If using beet, add ½ teaspoon sugar to the dressing to bring out the flavor.

salads

Salad of French Lentils and Broiled

or Barbecued Mushrooms

Salade de Lentilles et Champignons Grillé *A little marinating lets the flavors permeate the mushrooms and keeps them juicy during broiling or barbecuing.*

Serves 4

- ¾ cup French lentils
- 3 bay leaves
- 3 cups water
- 3 large flat mushrooms or portobellos
- 5 garlic cloves, chopped
- 3 shallots, chopped
- 3–5 Tbsp walnut oil
- 2–3 Tbsp balsamic or sherry vinegar
- salt and ground black pepper
- 2 Tbsp each chopped fresh parsley, and thyme or savory
- a handful of mixed salad greens

Preparation: 15-20 minutes

Cooking time : 1-1¼ hours

❶ Combine the lentils with the bay leaves and water, and bring to a boil. Reduce the heat and simmer, covered, for about 30–40 minutes. Drain well and discard the bay leaves.

❷ Remove the mushroom stems. Sprinkle the top of the mushrooms with about half of the garlic, shallots, walnut oil, vinegar, salt and pepper, and herbs.

❸ Heat the broiler or barbecue, and cook the mushrooms, skin side down, letting the juices accumulate in their caps. When they are tender and cooked through, remove from the heat and slice.

❹ Arrange a portion of lentils (they can be either warm or cool) on each plate. Toss the greens with a few spoonfuls of the remaining shallots, garlic, oil, vinegar, salt and pepper, and herbs, then arrange this on the plates next to the lentils. Arrange the mushrooms on each plate and sprinkle the remaining oil, vinegar, shallots, garlic, and herbs over it all. Serve immediately.

salads

Salad of Porcini, Avoli, Enoki, and Truffles

Insalata di Ovoli e Tartuffi *Sometimes I add fresh porcini to the ovoli, as both are sublime eaten raw. A handful of enoki, though not essential, is ever so appealing. Their long, graceful stems look terribly foresty, adding to the intensely fungi theme of this salad.*

The truffle topping can either be the white gems of Alba or the black nuggets of Norcia. If there is no fresh truffle, use truffle/porcini condiment or, as a last resort, drops of very fresh truffle oil.

SERVES 4

- 6 ovoli mushrooms or porcini, or 3 of each
- 1 celery stalk, cut into julienne strips
- 2½ oz enoki mushrooms, whole but separated
- 1–2 oz Parmesan cheese, cut into fine shavings
- juice of ½ lemon
- 4–6 Tbsp extra virgin olive oil
- 1 truffle, shredded, or several dollops of truffle/porcini condiment

Preparation: 15-20 minutes

❶ Slice the mushrooms very thinly, then toss with the celery, enoki, and Parmesan. Dress with lemon juice and olive oil.

❷ Sprinkle the top with the truffle or add the condiment to the salad, and serve, offering extra olive oil and lemon at the table.

salads

48

Ah, the thought of pasta and porcini. On my first visit to Florence, I was so obsessed with porcini that I soon gave up on gallery-going and planned my cultural forays by where the next dish of pasta al funghi was likely to be.

I have since found out that porcini is delicious not only on pasta, but in it as well. And it's not only porcini that is so terrific with pasta; nearly any type of mushroom is. Whether it is awash in a sauce of cream, tomatoes, butter, or olive oil, there are few things more utterly enticing.

pasta

Creamy Artichoke and Wild Mushroom Sauce

over Tagliatelle

Pappardelle con Carciofi e Funghi *Artichokes pair so easily, so happily, so very deliciously with porcini. Both taste of a forest in the Mediterranean, and both are very good when tossed with pasta.*

SERVES 4

- 2 artichokes
- 2–3 oz mixed dried wild mushrooms or 12 oz fresh mushrooms
- 1 onion, chopped
- 4 garlic cloves, roughly chopped
- 3 Tbsp butter, plus a little extra for buttering the pasta
- ½ cup hot water, if using dried mushrooms, or stock
- 1 cup light whipping cream
- ½ cup ricotta cheese or sour cream
- a few drops lemon juice
- salt and ground black pepper, to taste
- a few gratings of nutmeg
- 8 oz tagliatelle or egg lasagne sheets
- 2 cups shredded cheese, such as Gruyère, Emmentaler, Parmesan, asiago, dried Jack, or a combination

Preparation: 30 minutes
Cooking time : 15-20 minutes

❶ Snap the outer leaves off of the artichokes by bending them back crisply. When you reach the tender inner leaves, stop, and trim the base of the artichoke using a paring knife. Slice off the sharp prickly tops that are left, then cut each artichoke heart into quarters and pare out the thistle-like center.

❷ Blanch the artichoke hearts for about 3 minutes in boiling water to which you have added a squeeze of lemon. Remove, rinse in cold water, and, when cool enough to handle, slice thickly.

❸ If using dried mushrooms, rehydrate them, then remove from the water, squeeze dry, and cut into bite-size pieces. Reserve the mushroom liquid.

❹ Lightly sauté the onion and garlic in the butter until softened, then add the mushrooms and artichoke slices. Raise the heat and sauté, until the vegetables are lightly browned in spots.

❺ Pour in the mushroom liquid or stock, bring to a boil, and then reduce over high heat. Pour in the light whipping cream and cook a few minutes more.

❻ Lower the heat, stir in the ricotta cheese or sour cream, and the lemon juice, salt and pepper, and nutmeg. Set aside while you cook the pasta.

❼ Cook the pasta, according to the instructions on the package, until just tender. Drain carefully so as not to break too much of the pasta, then lightly toss with a little butter, and arrange on a platter.

❽ Pour the artichoke and mushroom sauce over, then blanket with the shredded cheese, and toss lightly. Serve immediately.

TIP:
Vary the mushrooms you use according to your personal taste and availability. Try porcini, chanterelles, morels, and other fragrant varieties.

Flat Thin Noodles with Porcini and

Mascarpone Cheese

Tagliatelle con Porcini e Mascarpone *Porcini, mascarpone cheese, and fresh Parmesan are served on tender pasta, with thin shreds of salty prosciutto. This dish is delicious with either fresh or dried porcini.*

SERVES 4 AS AN APPETIZER, 2 AS A MAIN COURSE

- 12 oz fresh porcini, or 2 oz dried porcini, rehydrated in ½ cup water, then squeezed dry
- 2 Tbsp butter
- 2 garlic cloves, chopped
- 2 Tbsp dry white wine
- 2 oz prosciutto, thinly sliced
- 12 oz tagliatelle or fettucine, preferably fresh
- 3–5 heaping tablespoons mascarpone cheese
- freshly shredded Parmesan cheese, to serve

Preparation: 10 minutes

Cooking time : 10 minutes

❶ Sauté the mushrooms in the butter with the garlic until just tender, then add the wine, and cook until it has nearly evaporated. Stir in the prosciutto and remove from the heat.

❷ Cook the pasta in rapidly boiling salted water, then drain, and toss it with the mushrooms, mascarpone, and Parmesan as desired. Serve in warmed shallow soup bowls, Italian-style, as they retain the heat and keep the pasta soft and supple.

TIP:

If using dried porcini, strain the soaking liquid carefully, then boil rapidly to reduce by about half, and add to the cooked pasta.

pasta

Penne with Mixed Mushrooms, Asparagus,

and Tomato-cream Sauce

Penne con Funghi, Asparagi, e Salsa Rossa *Sautéed mushrooms and asparagus pieces, simmered in a tomato-cream sauce, then tossed with quill-shaped penne and fresh basil, make a flavorful, rich Italian pasta.*

SERVES 4

- 1 onion, roughly chopped
- 4 garlic cloves, roughly chopped
- 3 Tbsp olive oil or butter, plus a little extra to finish
- 12 oz mixed mushrooms, cut into bite-size pieces
- salt and ground black pepper, to taste
- 1 lb fresh tomatoes, finely chopped, or 8 oz canned chopped tomatoes in their juice
- ¼–½ tsp sugar
- 1½ cups heavy cream
- 1–2 oz fresh sweet basil, torn
- 12–16 oz penne
- 1 bunch thin asparagus, tough ends broken off, cut into bite-size lengths
- 4–6 Tbsp shredded Parmesan cheese

Preparation: 30 minutes

Cooking time : 15 minutes

❶ Sauté the onion and garlic in the olive oil or butter, until softened. Then add the mushrooms and cook, stirring occasionally to prevent sticking. Season with salt and pepper, then pour in the tomatoes, and add the sugar. Bring to a boil and cook, stirring, a few minutes more. Then add the cream and about a third of the basil. Taste, adjust the seasoning if necessary, and remove from the heat.

❷ Cook the pasta until half done, then add the asparagus, and finish cooking. The pasta should be *al dente* and the vegetables just tender.

❸ Toss the hot pasta and asparagus with the creamy tomato-mushroom sauce, then toss with the Parmesan cheese, remaining basil, and a little extra olive oil or butter.

❹ Serve while piping hot on warmed plates.

pasta

Pasta with Mushrooms, Cream, and Fava Beans

Pasta alla Funghi e Fave *This rich, indulgent dish is given a fresh springtime touch with a garnish of delicate baby fava beans scattered around the edge of the plate. I like to include trompettes de la mort for the variety of color, shape, and texture they add, if I am using a mix of mushrooms. Or you could choose one particularly flavorful type, such as porcini or morels.*

SERVES 4
- 25–35 baby fava beans
- 1½–2 oz dried mushrooms
- 1 cup water or half water, half dry white wine or stock
- 1½ cups light cream
- 5 shallots, chopped
- 1 garlic clove, chopped
- 3–4 Tbsp butter
- a few gratings fresh nutmeg
- salt and ground black pepper, to taste
- 12–16 oz pasta
- freshly shredded Parmesan cheese, to serve

Preparation: 20-30 minutes
Cooking time: 20-30 minutes

❶ Combine the dried mushrooms with the measured liquid in a saucepan and bring to a boil. Reduce the heat and simmer for about 15 minutes, or until the mushrooms are very tender. Remove from the heat, and cut the mushrooms into bite-size pieces.

❷ Strain the mushroom liquid and return to the saucepan. Bring to a boil and reduce until syrupy. Add the cream and set aside.

❸ In a frying pan, lightly sauté the mushrooms, with the shallots and garlic in half the butter, then add this to the sauce along with a few gratings of nutmeg, and salt and black pepper.

❹ Cook the pasta in rapidly boiling salted water until *al dente*.

❺ Warm the fava beans in a little bit of the butter, and keep warm.

❻ Drain the pasta, then toss it with the sauce. Spoon into warmed, shallow soup bowls, Italian-style, and dot with the remaining butter. Scatter the fava beans around the bowls and the shredded Parmesan cheese over the top.

Pasta with Ham,

Dried Mushrooms, Tomatoes, and Ricotta Cheese

Trompettes de la mort, porcini, morels—are all terrific in this dish. I actually like this better with dried rather than with fresh, as both the tomato sauce and dried mushrooms are so deliciously highly flavored.

SERVES 4

- 4–5 scallions, thinly sliced
- 3–4 Tbsp olive oil
- ⅓ cup dry white wine
- 14 oz tomatoes, fresh or canned
- a pinch of sugar
- 2–3 oz ham, diced
- 2–3 Tbsp mixed dried mushrooms, broken into pieces
- 12 oz spaghettini
- 2 zucchini, thinly sliced
- 3 garlic cloves, chopped
- salt and ground black pepper, to taste
- ricotta cheese, to serve
- freshly shredded Parmesan, to serve

Preparation: 15-20 minutes

Cooking time : 30 minutes

❶ Lightly sauté the scallions in half the olive oil until softened. Pour in the white wine, and reduce to about 2 tablespoons, then add the tomatoes and sugar. Bring to a boil, then cook over medium heat for about 10 minutes. Add the ham and mushrooms, and continue to cook while you prepare the pasta and zucchini.

❷ Cook the spaghettini in rapidly boiling salted water until *al dente*.

❸ Meanwhile, sauté the zucchini in the remaining olive oil until lightly browned, then add the garlic, and remove from the heat. Season with salt and pepper.

❹ Drain the pasta, toss with the sauce, and then with the zucchini. Serve with the ricotta and Parmesan cheese in bowls for people to help themselves.

pasta

Flat Thin Noodles with Chicken Liver, Sausage,

and Mushroom Sauce

Tagliatelle con Fegatini *Classically this is made without garlic, but I often add it anyhow since it is my passion. If you decide to include garlic, add about 3 cloves, roughly chopped, when you are sautéeing the prosciutto or bacon.*

SERVES 4

- 1 onion, chopped
- 1 carrot, chopped
- 1 celery stalk with leaves, chopped
- 2 Tbsp chopped fresh parsley
- 3–4 Tbsp olive oil
- 5 chicken livers, washed and diced
- 4 oz prosciutto or 4 slices of bacon, diced
- 1 Italian sausage, preferably fennel flavored, cut into small pieces
- a handful of common cultivated mushrooms, quartered (optional)
- 1 oz dried mushrooms, preferably porcini, broken into small pieces
- ¾ cup stock
- ½ cup dry red wine
- 1½ lb tomatoes, fresh or canned, diced
- 1 bay leaf
- a pinch of sugar
- salt and ground black pepper, to taste
- several leaves fresh sage, thyme, and rosemary, chopped

- 1 lb fresh thin, flat noodle-type pasta, such as tagliolini, fettucine, or tagliatelle
- freshly shredded Parmesan cheese, to serve

Preparation: 15-20 minutes
Cooking time : 30-40 minutes

❶ Lightly sauté the onion, carrot, celery, and parsley in 3 tablespoons olive oil, then add the livers and a little more olive oil if you need it. Lightly brown the livers, stirring constantly.

❷ Add the proscuitto or bacon, the sausage, and the fresh mushrooms, if using. Cook a few moments, then add the dried mushrooms, stock, and wine. Cook over high heat for 5–10 minutes.

❸ Add the tomatoes, bay leaf, and sugar. Bring to a boil, then reduce the heat, and simmer over very low heat until the mixture thickens. Season with salt and pepper, as desired, and stir in the sage, thyme, and rosemary.

❹ Cook the pasta until *al dente*, then drain, and serve immediately with the sauce and a generous sprinkling of shredded Parmesan cheese.

pasta

56

Roasted Mushroom-topped Pasta with Cheese

When you eat the dish, you have a wonderful duet of the grated mushrooms melded into the pasta below and the accumulated juices of the mushrooms on top.

SERVES 4

- 1 lb small elbow macaroni
- 1 lb common cultivated, open-cap mushrooms
- 1 cup crème fraîche
- 1 cup ricotta cheese
- 2 shallots, chopped
- 2–3 tsp chopped fresh tarragon
- 3–4 oz freshly shredded Parmesan cheese
- 5 garlic cloves, chopped
- 6–8 oz shredded sharp Cheddar or fontina cheese
- 3–4 Tbsp butter
- salt and ground black pepper, to taste

Preparation: 20 minutes
Cooking time : 30 minutes

❶ Preheat a 400°F oven. Boil the macaroni until just *al dente* but still quite chewy. Drain and set aside.

❷ Shred the mushrooms then toss half of them with the cooked pasta. Add the crème fraîche, ricotta cheese, shallots, half the tarragon, the Parmesan, half the garlic, and the shredded Cheddar or fontina.

❸ Turn this mixture out into a round or square shallow baking pan. Remove the stems from the remaining mushrooms. Shred these and add them to the pasta, then shred the rest and spread over the top. Dot the mushrooms with the butter, then sprinkle with the

remaining garlic, tarragon, and salt and pepper.

❹ Bake for 20 minutes, or until the pasta is heated. Serve immediately.

pasta

57

Gratin of Macaroni with Wild Mushrooms
and Peas

Macaronis aux Champignons et Petits Pois, en Gratin Mushrooms and pasta are natural partners and make wonderful gratins. Add any sort of bright vegetable for variety and interest. When artichokes or asparagus are in season, they go into my gratin instead of the peas.

SERVES 4

- 2 oz small elbow macaroni
- 8 oz baby peas, fresh or frozen
- salt, to taste
- 8–12 oz mixed fresh wild mushrooms, or a mixture of ordinary white mushrooms and rehydrated dried mushrooms, diced
- 3 shallots, chopped
- 3 garlic cloves, chopped
- 3 Tbsp butter
- 3 Tbsp snipped fresh chives
- ground black pepper, to taste
- 3–4 Tbsp heavy cream
- 4–6 Tbsp each shredded fontina (or Gruyère, asiago, mild white Cheddar, or Jack) and Parmesan cheese

Preparation: 10 minutes
Cooking time : 30 minutes

❶ Preheat a 375°F oven. Cook the pasta in rapidly boiling salted water until it is about half tender, then remove from the heat, and drain. Toss with the peas. The pasta should be just short of *al dente* and the peas still bright green and perhaps a little crunchy.

❷ Sauté the mushrooms, shallots, and garlic in the butter until the mushrooms are lightly browned, then remove from the heat, and add the chives. Then toss with the pasta and peas. Season to taste.

❸ Layer half the pasta mixture in the base of a gratin or casserole dish, then drizzle with half the cream and half the cheese. Top with remaining pasta mixture and the remaining cheese, pouring the other half of the cream over the top.

❹ Bake in the oven for 20 minutes, or until the pasta is heated through and the cheese melted. If the pasta seems dry, add a bit more cream. Serve immediately.

pasta

58

Spaetzel with Mixed Mushrooms from the Fields

Dumplings and mushrooms have a natural affinity—you cannot but enjoy the combination, whatever kind of dumpling you make and whichever sort of mushroom you use.

SERVES 4

- 8-12 oz unbleached flour
- 1 tsp salt
- 2 eggs
- ½ cup milk
- several gratings of nutmeg
- 3–4 Tbsp butter
- 4–5 shallots or 1 onion, chopped
- 3 garlic cloves, chopped
- 8 oz mixed fresh mushrooms, such as field mushrooms, mousserons, porcini, and chanterelles, diced, or a combination of ordinary brown/white cultivated mushrooms mixed with several tablespoons rehydrated dried exotic mushrooms
- salt and ground black pepper, to taste
- 1 Tbsp chopped fresh parsley, to serve
- 1 Tbsp snipped fresh chives, to serve

Preparation: 30 minutes

Cooking time : 15 minutes

❶ Sift together the flour and salt. In a separate bowl, combine the eggs with the milk and nutmeg. Stir the liquid into the flour until you have a thick, very sticky batter.

❷ Bring a large pan of salted water to a boil then, using a spaetzel-maker or a colander with large holes set over the boiling water, pour in the batter and, using a large spoon, force it through the holes. The batter will form squiggly shapes that fall into the water. In about 5 minutes, tiny dumplings will bob up to the surface. Cover the pan and boil for 5 minutes more, removing the lid if the pan threatens to boil over.

❸ Drain the dumplings carefully, and place in a bowl of cold water for 15–30 minutes to firm up. Don't be tempted to omit this step or they will disintegrate into a sticky mess. You can keep them in water for up to 2 hours.

❹ Melt the butter, then sauté the shallots or onion. Add the garlic and mushrooms, and cook a few minutes until lightly browned and tender. Season with salt and pepper.

❺ When you are ready to serve, drain the spaetzels, and toss with the hot mushrooms. Heat through gently, adding a little extra butter if needed. Serve hot, with parsley and chives scattered over.

Spinach-ricotta Dumplings with

Mushroom Sauce

Gnocchi Verde con Funghi *Spinach-ricotta dumplings are delicious with all sorts of earthy wild mushroom sauces: lashings of cream and/or tomatoes, Madeira, and deep-flavored meat stock are all good enrichments. However simply sautéed mushrooms, with just a whiff of cream, are splendidly uncomplicated, and show off the mushrooms to perfection.*

SERVES 4

- 1 lb fresh spinach or 8 oz frozen
- 1 cup ricotta cheese
- 2 eggs, lightly beaten
- 6–8 Tbsp freshly shredded Parmesan cheese, plus a little extra
- 6–8 Tbsp flour, plus extra for rolling dumplings in
- salt and ground black or white pepper, to taste
- ⅛–¼ tsp freshly grated nutmeg
- ½ onion, chopped
- 3–4 Tbsp butter, olive oil, or a combination
- 3 garlic cloves, chopped
- 8 oz fresh wild mushrooms, such as porcini, ovoli, or mixed exotic mushrooms, sliced
- 2 Tbsp brandy or dry white wine
- 2 Tbsp crème fraîche or heavy cream
- 1 Tbsp chopped fresh Italian parsley

Preparation: 30 minutes
Cooking time : 35-40 minutes

❶ Cook the fresh spinach until just cooked through and bright green, then drain, squeeze dry, and chop. If using frozen chopped spinach, just defrost, drain, and squeeze well.

❷ Combine the spinach with the ricotta cheese, eggs, Parmesan cheese, flour, salt and pepper, and nutmeg. Chill for at least 2 hours. (The mixture should be firm enough to hold a ball shape when you form it with two spoons.)

❸ Preheat a 400°F oven. Using two spoons, form dumplings of the spinach mixture and roll each in flour. Poach the dumplings, in batches, in lightly boiling salted water. Cook the dumplings for 5–7 minutes, until they float, then take them out with a slotted spoon, and set aside in a gratin dish or baking pan.

❹ Sauté the onion in the butter and/or olive oil, then add the garlic and mushrooms, and cook until lightly browned. Add the brandy or wine and cook over high heat until evaporated. Stir in the crème fraîche, or cream, and parsley. Spoon the sauce over and around the dumplings. Sprinkle generously with shredded Parmesan, then bake for 15 minutes, or until the cheese is melted and lightly browned, and the dumplings are heated through. Serve immediately, with parsley scattered over.

Baked Lasagne with Creamy Porcini Sauce
and Chervil

Lasagne alla Porcini *This dish actually tastes best with the strong, concentrated flavor of dried, rather than fresh, porcini, and the mushroom liquid can then be used in the sauce. While most recipes are deliciously adaptable to nearly any fungi, use only porcini in this one, for the finest fragrance and flavor.*

Serves 4–6
- 2–3 oz dried porcini
- 2 cups water
- 5–8 shallots, chopped
- 5 Tbsp butter
- 3 Tbsp brandy
- 1½ cups light cream
- salt, ground black pepper, and a few gratings of nutmeg, to taste
- 10 oz lasagne noodles, preferably fresh
- 6–8 oz freshly shredded Parmesan cheese
- 3–5 Tbsp fresh chervil leaves, roughly chopped

Preparation: 1 hour

Cooking time : 1 hour

❶ Place the porcini and water in a saucepan and bring to a boil. Reduce the heat and simmer over medium heat for 5–10 minutes, or until the mushrooms have softened. Remove the mushrooms from the liquid, chop roughly, and set aside. Strain the liquid for the sauce.

❷ Sauté the shallots in the butter until softened, then add the mushrooms and cook for a few moments. Add the brandy, and cook over high heat until evaporated. It may flame, so avert your face.

❸ When the brandy has evaporated, ladle in ½ cup of the mushroom liquid, and cook over high heat until nearly evaporated. Repeat until all the liquid is used up and you have a concentrated, thin reduction. Now add the cream and simmer for 5–10 minutes. Season with salt, pepper, and nutmeg, and set aside.

❹ Preheat a 375°F oven. Cook the lasagne noodles in boiling salted water, a few at a time to keep them from sticking. (You can use fresh noodles without first cooking them, but I find that the result can be a bit heavy.)

❺ As they are cooked, carefully take each noodle out and immediately place in cold water. This will make them easier to handle. Then place them in a very lightly oiled pan. Repeat until all of the noodles are cooked.

❻ In a 12 inch x 15 inch buttered baking pan make a layer of lasagne noodles, letting the sheets hang over the sides to wrap over the layers of noodles as they are formed. Make a double layer, then ladle in about a quarter of the mushroom sauce, a quarter of the cheese, and a sprinkling of the chervil. Repeat until mixture is used up, ending with the cheese and reserving the final sprinkling of chervil until after the lasagne is baked.

❼ Bake in the oven for 25–30 minutes, or until the cheese is melted and lightly browned in places. Serve immediately, with the reserved chervil scattered over.

pasta

Mushroom-ricotta and Sausage Cannelloni

Cannelloni di Funghi e Salsicche *Diced, sautéed mushrooms added to ricotta cheese make delicious cannelloni. My secret for easy preparation is to use egg-roll wrappers. If dried porcini are unavailable, you may use ordinary common cultivated mushrooms, about 8–10 ounces, diced and sautéed, in their place.*

SERVES 4

- 3½ oz dried mushrooms, such as porcini
- 1 cup water
- 2 plump, 6-7oz, Italian sausages, roughly chopped
- 5–10 fresh common cultivated mushrooms, diced
- 5 garlic cloves, chopped
- 1½ cups ricotta cheese
- 6 Tbsp freshly shredded Parmesan cheese
- 1 egg, lightly beaten
- salt and ground black pepper, to taste
- several pinches of thyme and/or rosemary, as desired
- 8 egg-roll wrappers, approx. 6-8in. x 6-8in. or fresh pasta
- 2 lb fresh ripe tomatoes or 21 oz canned tomatoes with their juice, diced
- 6 oz mozzarella cheese, shredded
- 1-1½ Tbsp olive oil
- several handfuls fresh basil leaves, roughly torn

Preparation: 20-30 minutes

Cooking time : 30 minutes

❶ Place the dried mushrooms and the water in a saucepan and bring to a boil. Reduce the heat and simmer for about 5 minutes, then cover, and leave to plump up. When softened, remove the mushrooms from the pan and squeeze, saving the liquid. Roughly chop the mushrooms and strain the mushroom liquid.

❷ Meanwhile, cook the sausages with the fresh mushrooms until lightly browned in spots. Remove from the heat and mix with the garlic, rehydrated mushrooms, ricotta cheese, half the shredded Parmesan cheese, the egg, salt and pepper, and thyme and/or rosemary.

❸ Preheat a 375°F oven. Place several tablespoons of this mixture onto one edge of each pasta square, then roll each into a cylinder. Layer in the bottom of a 9- × 12-inch baking dish.

❹ Pour the diced tomatoes over the top, along with the mushroom liquid, then sprinkle with the mozzarella and remaining Parmesan cheese, and drizzle the olive oil over the top. Bake in the oven for 35–40 minutes, until the pasta is cooked, the liquid absorbed, and the cheese melted. Let stand a few moments, then serve, with the torn basil leaves scattered over.

pasta

64

Mixed Mushroom Dumplings

with Wild Mushroom and Chipotle Salsa

This cross-cultural dish of mushroom dumplings takes a walk on the wild side with its accompanying Wild Mushroom and Chipotle Salsa (see page 126). For a more sedate, classically European dish, serve it with Mushroom Jus (see page 127) instead.

SERVES 4

- 1 oz mixed dried mushrooms, including trompettes de la mort, porcini, mousserons, shiitakes, morels, and chanterelles
- 1 cup cottage cheese or ricotta cheese
- 2 small eggs, lightly beaten
- a few gratings of nutmeg
- 1–2 pinches fresh thyme leaves
- salt and ground black pepper, to taste
- 6 heaping tablespoons freshly shredded Parmesan cheese, plus a little extra
- 6 heaping tablespoons self-rising flour, plus extra for rolling dumplings in
- a drizzle of olive oil or a little butter, to finish

Preparation: 20-30 minutes
Cooking time : 25-30 minutes

❶ Place the mushrooms in a saucepan with 1 cup water to cover. Bring to a boil, reduce the heat, and simmer until the mushrooms are tender, about 5 minutes. Let stand in the hot water for about 15 minutes, then squeeze tightly, letting the juices drip back into the liquid.

❷ Roughly chop the mushrooms, then combine them with the cottage or ricotta cheese, the egg, nutmeg, thyme, and salt and pepper, the Parmesan and self-rising flour. The mixture should be thick and slightly stiff. Roll into 12 balls, rolling each in flour to form firm balls.

❸ Preheat a 400°–425°F oven or a hot broiler. Bring a pan of salted water to a boil, reduce the heat, and gently lower in the dumplings one at a time. The water should be gently boiling. The dumplings will fall to the bottom and quickly pop up again.

❹ Cover and cook gently, over medium-low heat, for 5–7 minutes. When cooked, take them out of the water and arrange them in a baking pan, preferably a ceramic one. Drizzle the top with olive oil, or dot with butter, and sprinkle with Parmesan cheese.

❺ Bake for 10 minutes or broil for about 5 minutes, or long enough to gratinée the dumplings. Serve the hot dumplings with a few spoonfuls of Mushroom and Chipotle Salsa.

pasta

Wild and cultivated mushrooms make marvelous
flavors to sauce or stew most any meats, poultry, or fish.
Many of the following sauces could be interchangeable:
try using pork in place of shrimp, or chicken in place of
veal anywhere.

Fillet Steak Sautéed with Mushrooms

in Sour Cream Sauce "alla Russe"

This lush, creamy, nutmeg-scented sauce, studded with chunks of barely cooked mushrooms and rare fillet steak, is one of my oldest favorite Russian-inspired mushroom dishes.

SERVES 4

- 1 large onion
- 3–5 Tbsp butter
- 8 oz common cultivated mushrooms, cut into big chunks or quartered
- 3 garlic cloves, chopped
- 8–12 oz beef fillet or fillet tail, cut into bite-size pieces
- 1 Tbsp flour
- ¾ cup each dry white wine and beef stock
- 1 cup crème fraîche or sour cream
- a generous pinch each freshly grated nutmeg and dried basil
- salt and black pepper, to taste
- a few drops lemon juice, if needed

Preparation: 15-20 minutes
Cooking time : 15-20 minutes

❶ Lightly sauté the onion in half the butter until softened, then remove from the pan, and set aside. Using any butter that is left behind, or adding a bit extra if needed, raise the heat and sauté the mushrooms and garlic in several batches until lightly browned but not cooked through. Place with the onion, along with any juices.

❷ Very quickly brown the meat to seal, letting it only sear and not cook through. Set aside on a plate.

❸ Melt any remaining butter in the same pan and sprinkle with the flour, letting it cook for a few minutes. Take off the heat, pour in the wine and stock, and stir well to let it thicken slightly. Boil to reduce to a concentrated sauce, then remove from the heat. Add the reserved mushrooms and onion, and crème fraîche or sour cream. Heat gently, then add nutmeg, basil, salt and pepper.

❹ Add the reserved steak and heat until just warmed through. Taste, and add lemon juice to balance the richness of the sauce, and more salt and pepper if necessary. Serve with spaetzel or brown rice.

Rosemary-roasted Veal

or Pork with Catalan-style Braised Mushrooms

Braised mushrooms, Catalan-style, added to the pan juices makes a luscious sauce for roasted meat, whether you choose veal or pork. Most any mushrooms are delicious, but you must use fresh tomatoes—canned won't do.

SERVES 6

- 2½ lb boned, lean veal or pork roasted (rolled, by the butcher, and tied, is excellent and will help it stay tidy during roasting)
- several sprigs fresh rosemary
- 10–12 garlic cloves, half cut into slivers, half chopped
- salt and ground black pepper, to taste
- 4 Tbsp olive oil
- 2 carrots, diced
- 10 garlic cloves, left whole but peeled
- 1 large onion, chopped
- 3 fresh ripe tomatoes, grated and skins discarded
- 1 lb mixed fresh wild mushrooms, or cultivated common mushrooms mixed with a few handfuls of dried mixed exotic mushrooms
- Dry white wine or stock, if needed

Preparation: 30 minutes
Cooking time : 3 hours

❶ Preheat a 350°F oven. Make incisions all over the meat. Into each one insert a sprig of rosemary that you have dipped into a little salt and a sliver of garlic. Stud the whole roast, then rub it with olive oil. Scatter the carrots, whole garlic cloves, and a few rosemary sprigs on the base of a roasting pan. Place the roast on a roasting rack, if you have one, or on the base of the pan. Place in the oven for 1 hour, 15 minutes.

❷ Meanwhile, sauté the onion slowly in the remaining olive oil, sprinkling with salt to draw out the juices, until soft, about 20 minutes. Stir in the chopped garlic, then add the tomatoes and raise the heat, cooking until the tomatoes melt into the onions, and the oil begins to separate. Add the mushrooms, reduce the heat, and cook over medium-low heat, stirring occasionally, until the mushrooms are cooked through. The moisture from the fresh mushrooms should rehydrate any dried ones used, but

if it doesn't, add a little stock or dry white wine to the pan, and boil until the mushrooms rehydrate.

❸ When the mushrooms are tender, season with salt and pepper, and set aside until the meat is ready. (A meat thermometer is useful here so that you can gauge the inside of the meat without cutting into it.)

❹ Remove the cooked veal or pork from its pan, pour off any fat from the surface but save any juices, then add a few tablespoons of wine or stock. Place on the stove and scrape the base of the pan. Add the braised mushrooms and warm through, then set aside and keep warm.

❺ Slice the roast, and serve each portion with a few spoonfuls of the mushroom sauce.

Sautéed Mixed Mushrooms

with Bacon, Chervil, and Watercress or Mâche
(Corn salad or lamb's lettuce)

This bistro-style dish is simple to prepare and marvelous for a winter supper. Any firm fleshy flavorful mushroom is fine; oyster mushrooms, chanterelles, trompette de la mort, and perhaps a few slices of porcini.

SERVES 4

- 1–1½ lb mixed fresh mushrooms, cut into bite-size pieces
- 3–4 Tbsp butter, or half butter and half olive oil
- 1 shallot, chopped
- 6 oz smoked bacon or good ham, such as prosciutto or jamon, cut into bite-size pieces
- 1 garlic clove, chopped
- a handful of watercress or mâche, roughly chopped
- 1 Tbsp chopped fresh chervil, tarragon, parsley, or a combination
- pain levain, to serve

Preparation: 10 minutes
Cooking time : 10-15 minutes

❶ Lightly sauté the mushrooms in the butter, or butter and olive oil, with the shallot and bacon or ham. When the mushrooms and bacon are browned, stir in the garlic, and cook for a few moments more. Serve garnished with the tufts of watercress or mâche, which will wilt slightly, and chopped herbs. Dig in with a chunk of pain levain.

Lamb Stew with Wild Mushrooms

Daube aux Champignons Sauvages *Once you've browned the meat and added everything else, the stew takes care of itself until you add the wild mushrooms. I like to add a few dried mushrooms into the pot along with the wine to boost the mushroom flavors and aromas.*

SERVES 6

- 1 carrot, chopped
- 2 leeks, chopped
- 3–4 Tbsp olive oil
- 3–3½ lb boneless lamb joint, such as a shoulder, with enough fat to keep it moist, cut into bite-size chunks
- salt, ground black pepper , and thyme, to taste
- flour, for dredging
- 14 oz tomatoes, fresh or canned, diced
- 3 bay leaves
- 1 cup beef stock
- 1 bottle robust red wine, such as a Merlot or Zinfandel
- 2–3 Tbsp dried wild mushrooms
- 1 garlic bulb, separated into cloves and peeled
- 12 oz mixed fresh wild mushrooms such as oyster, chanterelles, trompettes de la mort, mousserons, porcini, with a handful of common cultivated mushrooms, all cut into bite-size pieces
- 3–5 garlic cloves, chopped
- 1–2 Tbsp chopped fresh parsley

Preparation: 20 minutes

Cooking time : 3½-4 hours

❶ Sauté the carrot and leeks in the olive oil until softened, then place in a heavy-based casserole dish.

❷ Season the meat with salt, pepper, and thyme, then dredge with the flour, shaking off the excess. In the same pan used for the vegetables, brown the meat in a little olive oil for a few minutes, working in small batches so as not to crowd the pan. Place the meat into the casserole with the sautéed vegetables.

❸ Add the tomatoes, the bay leaves, beef stock, wine, dried mushrooms, and whole garlic cloves to the casserole. Bring to a boil, reduce the heat, and either simmer very gently on top of the stove or bake in a 325°F oven for about 3 hours.

❹ Remove from the stove or oven and let stand a few moments. Skim off the fat that has accumulated at the top. If the sauce is thin, pour it off into a saucepan and boil it to reduce. It might need 10–20 minutes, depending on how liquid it is.

❺ Meanwhile, sauté the fresh mushrooms in a tablespoon or two of the olive oil and season with salt and pepper, and the chopped garlic. Add to the meat, along with the mushroom juices.

❻ When the sauce has reduced, pour it back into the casserole with the meat and mushrooms. Return to the oven or the stove for about 15 minutes. Serve with the chopped parsley scattered over.

VARIATION:

Instead of lamb, this is an excellent dish for beef in the classic boeuf bourguignon style.

poultry, meat, & fish

Roasted Garlic Chicken with Porcini,

Cream, Pink Peppercorns, and Chervil

Poulet aux Cèpes *A golden brown chicken, its flesh infused with the scent of its garlic stuffing, is served in a creamy sauce rich with porcini, and sprinkled with pink peppercorns and chervil.*

If chervil is unavailable, use tarragon, chives, or parsley. If porcini are not available, use a mixed mushroom combination.

poultry, meat & fish

SERVES 4

- 1 chicken, about 2¼ lb
- salt and ground black pepper, to taste
- 3 Tbsp soft butter, duck fat, or olive oil
- ½ lemon, cut into several chunks
- 2 garlic bulbs, separated into cloves but left whole and unpeeled
- 3 Tbsp fresh tarragon or thyme
- 1 oz dried porcini
- 1 cup hot, but not boiling, water
- 2 shallots, chopped
- 1 cup dry white wine
- 1 cup chicken stock
- 1 cup crème fraîche or heavy cream
- 1 Tbsp pink peppercorns
- 2–3 Tbsp chopped fresh chervil

Preparation: 15 minutes

Cooking time : 1½ hours

❶ Preheat a 325°F oven. Place the chicken in a roasting pan and rub its insides and outsides with salt, pepper, and about half the butter, duck fat, or olive oil. Fill its insides with the lemon chunks, about half of the whole garlic cloves, and the tarragon or thyme. Scatter the rest of the garlic cloves around the chicken.

❷ Roast the chicken for about an hour, or until golden brown and just tender. Remove from the oven and let stand for 10 minutes to rest before carving. Meanwhile, make the porcini sauce.

❸ Rehydrate the dried porcini by putting them in a bowl with the hot water. Let stand for 30 minutes, remove, squeeze, and save the mushroom liquid.

❹ Lightly sauté the mushrooms in the remaining butter, duck fat, or olive oil, with the chopped shallots. Add the mushroom liquid, wine, and stock, and reduce over high heat to about 1 cup in total. Add the crème fraîche or cream, reduce the heat, and simmer until thickened, about 20 minutes.

❺ When the chicken has roasted and stood for 10 minutes, carve it, and keep warm.

❻ Carefully skim the fat from the pan juices, then stir the warm mushroom sauce into the pan, scraping the base to release all the rich crusty bits. If the base of the pan is too crusty, pour a little stock or white wine in first, cook through and deglaze to release the bits, and then add the mushroom sauce.

❼ Serve the chicken surrounded by the roasted garlic cloves and blanketed by the porcini sauce. Scatter over pink peppercorns and chervil, and serve immediately.

TIP:

Save the chicken carcass to make stock to use in soups and sauces.

Pan-sautéed Chicken with Morel Mushrooms

Poulet aux Morilles You can make this with all breasts or all dark meat if you like, and similarly, you can roast or broil the chicken pieces before adding them to your sauce if you don't feel like sautéeing.

SERVES 4–6

- 1 oz dried morels
- 2 cups water
- 1 chicken, about 3 lb, cut in serving pieces
- salt and ground black pepper, to taste
- 2 Tbsp olive oil
- 1 oz butter, preferably sweet
- 3–5 shallots, chopped
- 3 Tbsp brandy or Marsala
- 1 cup crème fraîche or sour cream, stirred with a few tablespoons of heavy cream and a squeeze of lemon juice
- 2 Tbsp chopped fresh chervil, parsley, or snipped fresh chives

Preparation: 30-40 minutes

Cooking time : 1 hour

❶ Place the morels and the water in a saucepan and bring to a boil. Cook over medium heat until tender, and the liquid turns brown and thickens. After 20–30 minutes, it should have reduced by about half. Remove from the heat, take the morels out of the liquid, and place on a plate. Strain the liquid through a cheesecloth or pour off the top and leave behind the grit.

❷ Rub the chicken pieces with salt and pepper, then sauté them in the olive oil and butter until lightly browned. You will need to do this in batches. Remove to a casserole or plate as you cook them.

❸ When the chicken pieces are all browned, pour off all the fat except for about 1 tablespoon, then sauté the shallots. Return the chicken to the pan, and pour in the brandy or the Marsala, taking care to avert your face when it flames. Remember not to pour it straight from the bottle. Mix the crème fraîche or sour cream with the

mushroom liquid and mushrooms, and add to the pan.

❹ Cook over low heat for about 25 minutes, or until the chicken is cooked through. You may like to keep the white meat portions out of the pan for the first 10 minutes, since the dark meat requires longer cooking, and the white meat will overcook and grow dry if left on the heat too long.

❺ Serve each portion with a few spoonfuls of sauce, and a sprinkling of fresh herbs.

Chicken Breasts, Stuffed with Wild Mushroom

Duxelles, in Cream Sauce

Poulet aux Champignons, Sauce à la Crème *The light creamy flesh of chicken breast is the perfect vehicle for enjoying the strong foresty scent and taste of wild mushrooms.*

SERVES 4

- 3 oz mixed dried mushrooms
- 1½ cups water
- 4 boned chicken breast halves
- 2 shallots, chopped
- 3 garlic cloves, chopped
- salt and ground black pepper, to taste
- juice of ¼ lemon
- 2 Tbsp dry white wine
- 1 Tbsp olive oil
- 1 cup chicken stock
- 3 Tbsp butter
- ½ cup light cream
- 1 Tbsp each chopped fresh chervil and snipped fresh chives, to garnish (optional)

Preparation: 20-30 minutes
Cooking time : 15 minutes

❶ Place the mushrooms and water in a saucepan and bring to a boil. Reduce the heat and simmer for about 15 minutes. Remove them from the liquid and chop roughly.

❷ Cut a pocket in each chicken piece, then marinate with half the shallots, garlic, salt and pepper, lemon juice, white wine, and olive oil. Let stand while you prepare the duxelle filling and sauce.

❸ Strain the mushroom liquid and reduce to about ½ cup. Add the chicken stock and remaining wine, and reduce to about 1 cup until thin but saucelike. Set aside.

❹ Sauté the mushrooms with the remaining shallots and garlic in 2 tablespoons of the butter. Add a spoonful or two of the sauce, then continue to cook the mushrooms until they form a dryish filling. Remove from the heat and season.

❺ Remove the chicken breasts, saving the marinade, and stuff each breast with a few spoonfuls of the mushroom mixture. Seal tightly with a toothpick or two, or a bamboo skewer. Set aside.

❻ Heat the pan, add the remaining butter, then sauté the chicken breasts on each side for 3 minutes.

❼ Remove the chicken from the pan and pour in any remaining marinade, the sauce, and the cream. Stir until the mixture cooks through, about 5 minutes.

❽ Serve the chicken breasts, with their sauce, garnished with the chervil and chives.

Chicken or Turkey "Bitkies"

SERVES 4–6

- 2¼ lb ground chicken or turkey
- 10–15 garlic cloves, roughly chopped
- 2 cups fresh bread crumbs
- 2 eggs, lightly beaten
- 1–2 Tbsp chopped fresh parsley, plus extra to garnish
- 1 Tbsp chopped fresh tarragon (optional)
- 2 tsp capers
- 12 oz fresh mushrooms
- salt and ground black pepper, to taste
- oil or butter, for sautéeing
- 5 shallots, chopped
- ½ cup dry white wine or stock, or a combination
- ½ cup light cream
- 1 cup crème fraîche or sour cream
- a squeeze of lemon, if needed

Ground chicken or turkey is mixed with shredded raw mushrooms in this Russian-inspired dish, then seasoned with parsley, tarragon, capers, and lots and lots of garlic. The patties are then fried, and served with a creamy mushroom sauce.

Preparation: 10 minutes

Cooking time : 15-20 minutes

❶ Combine the chicken or turkey, garlic, bread crumbs, eggs, parsley, tarragon, and capers. Shred about 4 ounces of the mushrooms. Add to mixture, season with salt and pepper, and form into patties.

❷ Brown the patties, in batches, in a heavy-based frying pan in a tiny bit of oil or butter, taking care that they do not fall apart. As they are cooked, transfer to a plate or pan, and keep warm.

❸ Pour off all the fat except for about a tablespoon, and in this lightly sauté the shallots and remaining mushrooms until softened. Then pour in the wine and/or stock, and reduce to a few tablespoons. Stir in the cream and crème fraîche or sour cream, taste for seasoning, and return the patties to the sauce. Season with salt, pepper, and, if needed, a squeeze of lemon. Sprinkle with parsley and serve immediately.

Morel and Chicken Pie

SERVES 4

- 1½ oz dried morel mushrooms
- 1 cup water or stock
- 3 shallots, chopped
- 2 garlic cloves, chopped
- 3 Tbsp butter
- 3 Tbsp brandy
- salt and white pepper, to taste
- 2 chicken thighs or dark meat,

For this dish, other mushrooms are fine in place of the morels—porcini, especially so, or a foresty mixture. And, you can vary the vegetables too—leeks or asparagus, tiny blanched turnips, or new potatoes are all good choices. Sweetbreads or chicken livers also make good additions to this mixture.

  boned and diced
- 2 boneless chicken breasts, cut into bite-size pieces
- 2 Tbsp flour
- ⅓ cup heavy cream

- a grating of nutmeg
- 1½ lb puff pastry

Preparation: 40-50 minutes

Cooking time : 30-45 minutes

poultry, meat & fish

76

❶ Rehydrate the mushrooms in the water or stock in a saucepan. Bring to a boil, then simmer over low heat for about 5 minutes. Leave to soak until cool enough to handle, about 20 minutes. Squeeze out the mushrooms, reserving the liquid. Chop the mushrooms and set aside. Strain the liquid and set aside.

❷ Lightly sauté the chopped mushrooms with the shallots and garlic in about half the butter, until the mushrooms are just tender and lightly browned. Add the brandy, taking care to avert your face in case it flames, and cook over high heat for a few moments. Season with salt and pepper, and set aside.

❸ Season the chicken meat with salt and pepper, then toss it in flour. Lightly brown in the remaining butter. Do not cook the meat through, only let it turn light golden on the outside, then remove it from the pan.

❹ Preheat a 400°F oven. Into the pan add the mushroom liquid, reduce by about half, then add the cream, and pour in any liquid that has accumulated from the mushrooms. Cook over high heat until the mixture thickens again. Season with the nutmeg, salt, and pepper.

▲ *Morel and Chicken Pie*

❺ Combine the sauce with the mushrooms and chicken, then pour into either one large or four individual pie dishes.

❻ Roll out the pastry and cover the pie(s), sealing the edges of the crust to the pie dish. Bake in the oven for about 25 minutes, or until the top of the pastry is golden or lightly brown and crisply puffy. Serve immediately.

TIP:
Instead of just dried morel mushrooms, use 2 oz mixed dried mushrooms, or
8 oz common cultivated mushrooms with 1 oz dried morels, or 10 oz fresh morels or other wild mushrooms. If you are not using dried mushrooms, you will need 1 cup stock for the sauce.

poultry, meat & fish

Salmon with Trompettes de la Mort

Saumon aux Trompettes de la Mort *Trompettes de la mort translate as "trumpets of death" from the French. They are thus named for their blackish color, not because of any danger! They are not only safe, they are delectable, a favorite in the Jura mountains in the west of France where they are layered with potatoes for spectacular gratins.*

Their black color looks particularly fine with the pale pink of salmon. If you can find black chanterelles or trompettes de la mort fresh, do use them, and, if you cannot, use dried ones. Yellow chanterelles can be combined with the black chanterelle or trompettes de la mort, and will taste lovely but not look so striking as the all-black.

SERVES 4
- 1½ lb salmon fillets
- salt and ground black pepper, to taste
- juice of ¼ lemon
- 12 oz fresh trompettes de la mort, black chanterelles, or chanterelles, or use 1 oz dried trompettes de la mort or black chanterelles
- 4 Tbsp butter
- 4 shallots, chopped
- 1 garlic clove, chopped
- ½ cup each dry white wine and fish stock
- ¼ cup heavy cream or crème fraîche

Preparation: 15 minutes
Cooking time : 15-20 minutes

❶ Sprinkle the salmon with salt, pepper, and lemon juice. Set aside while you cook the mushrooms.

❷ Cut the mushrooms into bite-size pieces. If using dried mushrooms, place them in a saucepan with the white wine and bring to a boil. Reduce the heat, simmer for about 5 minutes, then let stand and plump up. Remove from the wine, and squeeze dry, saving the mushroom liquid. Cut the mushrooms into bite-size pieces and set aside. Strain the wine and set aside.

❸ Melt half the butter and sauté the fresh or rehydrated mushrooms, shallots, and garlic until softened. Season with salt and pepper, then add the wine and fish stock. Bring to a boil, cook over high heat until reduced by about half, then stir in the cream or crème fraîche. Taste for seasoning and set aside to keep warm.

❹ Melt the remaining butter and reserve a tablespoon. Cook the bottom (skin side) of the salmon fillets. Brush the tops with the reserved melted butter, and place under the broiler to cook the top, 1–2 minutes.

❺ Reheat the sauce, if necessary, and spoon it onto warmed plates, then top each with a portion of the sautéed salmon and serve.

poultry, meat, & fish

香米

Shrimp and Scallops with Mushrooms

in Spicy Thai Sauce

You can make this with just shrimp or just scallops instead of both, or with chicken breast, or tofu instead. Often I expand the dish with more and more vegetables, depending on what is available.

Serve in a soup bowl with a spoonful of rice or a tangle of rice noodles alongside, to soak up the rich, spicy sauce.

SERVES 4

- 10 dried mixed mushrooms such as shiitake, or Chinese black mushrooms
- 10 each dried small and large black fungus (tree cloud)
- 2 cups stock
- 5 shallots, chopped
- 5 garlic cloves, chopped
- 3 Tbsp vegetable oil
- ½ tsp each turmeric and curry powder
- 1 tsp ground coriander
- 1 Tbsp chopped fresh ginger root
- 1 medium-hot fresh red chile such as jalapeño, thinly sliced
- 1 carrot, sliced diagonally
- ¼ eggplant, cut into small bite-size pieces or diced
- ¼ red pepper, chopped
- 4–5 oz common cultivated mushrooms, cut into bite-size pieces
- 3–4 kaffir lime leaves, fresh or dried
- 10–12 spears very thin asparagus, cut into bite-size lengths
- 3½ oz creamed coconut, in small pieces
- 8 each large shrimp and scallops, trimmed and halved or quartered
- juice of ½ lime, or as desired

Preparation: 15-20 minutes
Cooking time : 15-20 minutes

❶ Place the shiitake or Chinese black mushrooms and two types of black fungus in a saucepan with the stock. Bring to a boil, reduce the heat, and simmer for about 5 minutes. Cover and leave while you prepare the rest of the dish.

❷ Lightly sauté the shallots and garlic in the vegetable oil until softened, then sprinkle in the turmeric, curry powder, coriander, ginger, chile, carrot, eggplant, red pepper, and the rest of the mushrooms, and cook until the vegetables are half tender, about 5 minutes.

❸ Remove the rehydrated mushrooms and fungus from the stock. Cut the large black fungus into smaller pieces, leaving the

smaller fungus and the mushrooms whole. Strain the mushroom liquid.

❹ Pour the strained liquid into the sautéeing vegetables, along with the lime leaves, and cook a few minutes together, then add the rehydrated mushrooms and fungus, the asparagus, shrimp, and scallops. Stir well but gently, and add the creamed coconut, tossing gently over medium heat until the coconut has emulsified into the sauce. The asparagus and seafood should be just cooked through. Serve immediately, with a squeeze of lime.

VARIATION:
Thai Curry with Tomatoes and Flour Tortillas
Add 5–8 ripe tomatoes, diced, to the simmering vegetables, canned is fine. Serve with warmed flour tortillas to dip into the spicy mixture and to wrap up bits of vegetables and seafood.

poultry, meat, & fish

81

Russian Fish Stuffed with Mushrooms

Rizhskoye Telnoye *This dish is classic French-inspired Russian, full of aristocratic flavors and luxe ingredients.*

SERVES 4

For the stuffed fish fillets
- 4 thin fish fillets such as flounder or plaice, about 6 oz each
- salt and ground black pepper
- 10–12 oz common cultivated mushrooms, brown or white, or field mushrooms, chopped
- 3 shallots, chopped
- 1 garlic clove, chopped
- 2 Tbsp chopped fresh parsley
- 4 Tbsp butter
- 3–4 Tbsp heavy cream, crème fraîche, or sour cream
- a few gratings of nutmeg
- 1 cup each fish or chicken stock, dry white wine or vermouth

For the sauce
- 1 Tbsp butter
- 1 Tbsp flour
- poaching liquid from above, adding more stock or wine/vermouth if needed
- ½ cup heavy cream, crème fraîche, or sour cream
- salt and ground black pepper
- 1 egg yolk
- juice of ½ lemon
- 1 Tbsp snipped fresh chives

- 3–4 Tbsp shredded Gruyère and Parmesan cheese

Preparation: 30 minutes

Cooking time : 15 minutes

---

❶ Place the fish fillets between sheets of waxed paper and pound them gently into flat scallops. Season, and set aside.

❷ Sauté the mushrooms, shallots, garlic, and parsley until lightly browned, about 10–15 minutes. Add the cream, crème fraîche, or sour cream. Cook over high heat to form a thickish paste. Season with nutmeg, salt, and pepper.

❸ Spoon one quarter of the mushrooms onto each fillet. Roll up, and close with toothpicks.

❹ Place the stuffed fish fillets in a heavy-based frying pan along with the stock and wine or vermouth. Bring to a boil, then cook over very low heat until the fish is no longer opaque on the outside and barely cooked through.

❺ Remove the stuffed fish fillets to a gratin baking dish. Any bits of mushroom or fish that have fallen into the poaching liquid will enrich it. If too much stuffing has fallen out, simply spoon it back in.

❻ Boil the poaching liquid until it reduces to 1¼ cups, 7–10 minutes.

❼ Preheat a 400°F oven. Make the sauce; melt the butter, sprinkle in the flour, and let cook a minute or two. Remove from the heat and stir in the hot reduced stock all at once, then return to the heat and stir together until thickened. In a bowl, stir together the egg yolk and cream, crème fraîche, or sour cream, lemon juice, and chives.

❽ Stir a little of the hot sauce into this, then stir this back into the hot sauce, and pour it over the stuffed fish fillets. Sprinkle with cheese, then place in the oven and bake about 10 minutes or until fish is hot and the top is crisp and lightly browned. Serve hot.

Almost every mushroom is delicious with eggs: you can count on a buttery little scramble to bring out the best in your fungi. Tuck sautéed mushrooms into an omelet, or splash them into a sauce and lavish them onto poached eggs. If you are ever in doubt about what to do with a cache of extravagant fungi, you can't go far wrong with a basketful of fresh eggs and a frying pan.

eggs

Omelet with Mousserons

Omelette aux Mousserons *This omelet from southwestern France has a real "gout d'automne," the flavor of the fall, with its woodsey mushrooms. If you do not have mousserons, use any flavorful mushrooms, especially porcini, or a mixture of common cultivated brown mushrooms mixed with a few tablespoons of delicious dried mushrooms.*

Though in southwestern France they would traditionally use the fat from a duck or goose for this dish, I tend to favor olive oil or butter.

SERVES 4

- 12 oz mousserons, diced
- 1 slice (about 2 oz) prosciutto, jamon, or other strong-flavored raw ham, diced
- 3 garlic cloves, chopped
- 1–2 Tbsp chopped fresh parsley
- 2–3 Tbsp olive oil or butter
- salt and ground black pepper, to taste
- 8–10 eggs, lightly beaten
- 2–4 Tbsp milk

Preparation: 20-25 minutes

Cooking time : 10 minutes

❶ Lightly sauté the mushrooms together with the ham, garlic, and parsley, in about half the olive oil or butter, until just tender. Season with salt and pepper, and set aside.

❷ Combine the eggs with the milk.

❸ Heat a small omelet pan for four individual omelets or a large pan for one large or two medium-size omelets. For four individual omelets, add a teaspoon or two of olive oil or butter to the hot pan, then pour in a quarter of the egg mixture. Cook a few moments, as for a rolled omelet, then spoon in a quarter of the mushroom mixture. Roll the sides over and roll the omelet out of the pan. Repeat with the remaining ingredients. For one large omelet, do the same, using all the egg and filling in one go. For two medium-size omelets, do the same, using half the mixtures for each. Serve immediately.

eggs

Eggs Baked in a Ramekin with Cream

and Sautéed Mushrooms

Oeufs en Cocotte aux Champignons Plump eggs rest on top of a bed of sautéed mushrooms, and more or less poach in the oven, nestled beneath a cream and cheese topping.

Sometimes I use the sauce for poached eggs rather than making individual ramekins.

SERVES 4

- 5 shallots, chopped
- 3 garlic cloves, chopped
- 3 Tbsp butter
- 4 oz fresh mushrooms, preferably a mixture of wild or exotic, roughly chopped or diced
- 3 Tbsp Cognac or brandy
- 3 Tbsp dry white wine
- 1 cup crème fraîche or heavy cream
- a grating of nutmeg
- salt, to taste
- 1 tsp fresh thyme
- 4 or 8 eggs, depending on whether each person will have one or two
- 6 oz mild cheese, such as comte, Gruyère, Emmentaler, or a combination of any of these, plus Parmesan, shredded

Preparation: 10 minutes
Cooking time : 30 minutes

❶ Preheat a 400°F oven. Lightly sauté the shallots and garlic in the butter, then add the mushrooms, and cook until lightly browned, about 10 minutes. Pour in the Cognac or brandy (averting your face as you do), cook over high heat until evaporated, then add the wine, and cook a few minutes more. Stir in the crème fraîche or cream, the nutmeg, salt, and thyme, and set aside.

❷ Into the base of four individual ramekins, place a tablespoon or so of the mushrooms. Top with one or two eggs slid right on top of the mushrooms without scrambling them in any way, then sprinkle with the cheese.

❸ Bake in the oven for 10–15 minutes, or long enough to cook the eggs through. Serve immediately.

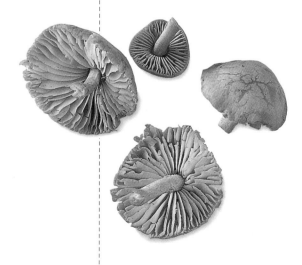

Eggs in Red Wine Sauce

with Braised Mushrooms

Oeufs en Meurette aux Champignons *Poached eggs, blanketed in red wine and mushroom sauce, make a delectable dish for either brunch or a bistro-style supper. The dish is vegetarian as is, but for omnivores, garnish with a handful of crisply browned diced bacon, or pancetta.*

SERVES 4

- 1 bottle red wine, such as a Côtes de Rhône, Cahors, Cabernet, or Zinfandel
- 2 cups stock
- 3 cloves
- 1 bay leaf
- a few sprigs fresh thyme
- 1 leek, including the green part, diced
- 3 garlic cloves, roughly chopped
- 1 celery stalk, diced
- 2 carrots, chopped
- 1 Tbsp tomato paste
- 4 Tbsp butter
- 8 oz mixed fresh mushrooms
- 3 Tbsp flour
- a few drops balsamic vinegar
- 4 or 8 eggs, depending on whether each person will have one or two
- 1–2 tsp vinegar for poaching

Preparation: 20-30 minutes

Cooking time : 1½-2 hours

❶ Combine the wine, stock, cloves, bay leaf, thyme, leek, garlic, celery, and carrots in a saucepan and bring to a boil. Cook over medium-high heat for about an hour, or until reduced by about half. The vegetables should be very, very tender by now. If they are not, continue cooking until they are. Mix in the tomato paste, then pour the sauce through a strainer, pushing on the solids to extract all the juices, leaving behind only the fibrous parts which you should discard.

❷ Melt the butter in a heavy-based frying pan and sauté the mushrooms until lightly browned. Then sprinkle with the flour and add the wine sauce, stirring as you pour it in. You may need to transfer this to a large casserole or heavy-based saucepan to accommodate all the mushrooms and sauce.

❸ Simmer the mixture for about 30 minutes, letting the mushrooms braise in the sauce.

❹ When you are ready to serve, poach the eggs in just simmering water to which you have added the vinegar. Do not salt the water; that makes the eggs ragged, whereas vinegar holds them together.

❺ Lift the eggs from their poaching liquid, dry on a paper towel or a clean dish towel, then place on warmed plates, and serve with the mushroom wine sauce. Eat immediately.

TIP:

I like to include oyster mushrooms, chanterelles, trompettes de la mort, and porcini in this recipe. If you like, you can add some common cultivated mushrooms as well.

Wild and tamed mushrooms taste wonderful with all manner of grains. The grains seem to balance the strong earthy flavors of the fungi delightfully, whether they are light rices stirred into risotti, hefty buckwheat or barley of Eastern Europe, or fine long grain rices of the Far East.

grains

Kasha-varnichkes

with Wild Mushrooms and Sautéed Onions

This tastes of childhood dinners prepared by Russian or Polish mamas and grandmas, even if you yourself have been nowhere near Eastern Europe.

Kasha is utterly delicious eaten with nearly any kind of sautéed mushroom. I like to stuff pasta with kasha and fried onions sometimes, and serve it in a sauce of sautéed mushrooms with sour cream and a scent of nutmeg.

This dish is delicious just as is, though meatballs in a little sour cream sauce alongside would make a feast fit for a czar, as you might say!

SERVES 4

- 8 oz kasha
- 6 oz butterfly shaped pasta or other short noodle shapes
- 1 oz dried porcini or other wild mushroom mix
- 2½ cups chicken or vegetable stock
- 3 onions, chopped or sliced
- 3–5 Tbsp vegetable oil
- 2–3 Tbsp butter
- 10–12 oz common cultivated mushrooms, sliced
- sour cream or yogurt, to serve (optional)

Preparation: 20-30 minutes
Cooking time : 45 minutes

❶ Lightly toast the kasha in a heavy-based, ungreased saucepan until it smells toasty and turns light nutty brown. Remove from the heat and set aside.

❷ Cook the pasta in rapidly boiling salted water until just tender, then drain well, and rinse with cold water. Drain again and set aside.

❸ Simmer the dried mushrooms in the stock for about 15 minutes, or until tender, then remove from the heat. Take the mushrooms out of the liquid and set aside. Strain the liquid and add to the kasha.

❹ Place the kasha on the stove and bring to a boil. Reduce the heat to low, cover, and simmer until the liquid is absorbed, about 15 minutes.

❺ Meanwhile, cook the onions in the oil and butter until softened and browned, about 15 minutes. Add the rehydrated and cultivated mushrooms, and cook until browned and tender. Season with salt and pepper.

❻ Combine the kasha with the pasta and onion-mushroom mixture. Check for seasoning and serve hot, with sour cream or rich yogurt on the side, if desired.

Mixed Mushroom Pilaf

SERVES 4

with Truffle or Porcini Oil

- 3 shallots, chopped
- 2 garlic cloves, chopped
- 2–3 Tbsp butter
- 1½ cups long grain rice
- 3¾ cups chicken or vegetable stock
- 8 oz mixed fresh mushrooms or 2–3 oz mixed dried mushrooms, rehydrated and squeezed dry, diced
- a drizzle of truffle oil or 1 Tbsp porcini oil
- 1–2 Tbsp fresh snipped chives

Preparation: 15 minutes

Cooking time : 20 minutes

Lightly butter-toasted grains of rice are perfumed with the foresty scent of mushrooms. This is lovely with scallops of veal or chicken breast lightly cooked over a wood fire, or trout wrapped in grape leaves and bacon then barbecued.

❶ In a large saucepan, lightly sauté the shallots and garlic in the butter until softened. Do not brown.

❷ Set aside half the shallot mixture from the pan. Then gently cook the rice in the remaining mixture until golden. Stir in the stock, lower the heat, and cover tightly. Cook until the rice is almost tender, about 6–8 minutes.

❸ Meanwhile, place the remaining shallot mixture in a frying pan and sauté the mushrooms in it. When the rice is almost tender and still just slightly soupy, toss in the sautéed mushrooms, cover, and continue to cook over low heat 3–4 minutes more, or until the rice grains are just tender.

❹ Fluff the rice up with a fork, then serve immediately, drizzled with the truffle or porcini oil, and with the chives scattered over.

Polenta with meaty tomato-mushroom sauce

SERVES 4–6

- 1 onion, chopped
- 1 carrot, chopped
- 1 celery stalk, including the leaves, chopped
- 2 Tbsp olive oil
- 5 garlic cloves, roughly chopped
- 2 Tbsp chopped fresh parsley
- 2 cups lean ground beef
- 3–4 slices of bacon, diced
- 1 cup dry red wine
- 1 cup beef stock
- 2 oz dried mushrooms,

Polenta al Ragù di Funghi *Hearty mushrooms enrich this tomatoey sauce for polenta. If you have a couple of Italian sausages, add them to your sauce with, or in place of, the ground beef.*

preferably porcini, broken into small pieces
- 2 lb fresh ripe tomatoes or 2 × 14-oz cans tomatoes, diced
- 2 Tbsp tomato paste
- 2 bay leaves
- a pinch of sugar (optional)
- salt and ground black pepper, to taste

- 3–5 Tbsp fresh basil leaves, lightly crushed or chopped
- 4 cups polenta
- 6¼ cups water, or more if needed
- freshly shredded Parmesan cheese, a few gratings of nutmeg, and butter as desired, to serve

grains

▲ *Polenta al Ragù di Funghi*

❶ In a large saucepan, sauté the onion, carrot, and celery in the olive oil until softened, then stir in the garlic, parsley, beef, and bacon. Continue cooking, breaking up the meat with a fork, until it is no longer pink, then pour in the wine, and cook over high heat until nearly all the liquid has evaporated.

❷ Add the stock, mushrooms, tomatoes, tomato paste, bay leaves, sugar (if using), salt and pepper, and basil leaves. Bring to a boil, then reduce the heat, and simmer until the sauce is thickened, about an hour.

❸ Meanwhile cook the polenta. Mix the polenta with ½ cup cold water and let stand a few minutes. Bring the remaining water to a boil, then add a pinch of salt, and, using a wooden spoon, slowly stir in the water-swollen polenta.

❹ Cook over low heat for about 40 minutes, stirring as often as you can. It will sputter and spit, and, if it isn't stirred regularly, it will burn and stick to the base too. Add more water if needed. Polenta is done when it is a thick and creamy porridge consistency.

❺ Stir in a generous sprinkling of Parmesan cheese, a dash of nutmeg, and butter as desired, then serve with the tomato-mushroom sauce ladled over it, and a final sprinkling of Parmesan.

grains

Rich Risotto of Many Mushrooms

A wide variety of mushrooms is what gives this risotto its charm. Instead of basil, try serving the risotto with a finishing of shaved truffles, or more prosaically, a little chive butter.

Serves 4

- 12–16 oz mixed fresh mushrooms, or common cultivated mushrooms combined with 2–3 oz rehydrated dried mushrooms, diced
- 5–6 Tbsp butter, olive oil, or a combination
- 5–8 shallots, chopped
- 3–5 garlic cloves, chopped
- 1 cup Arborio rice
- 1 cup dry white wine
- a grating of nutmeg
- 3¾ cups stock, or as needed
- ½ cup light cream (optional)
- 4–6 Tbsp freshly shredded Parmesan cheese, plus extra to serve
- a few basil leaves, thinly sliced, to garnish

Preparation: 20-30 minutes
Cooking time : 40 minutes

❶ Sauté the mushrooms in the butter and/or olive oil, until softened, then add the shallots and garlic. Cook a few minutes, then add the rice, and cook, stirring, until it begins to turn golden.

❷ Stir in the wine and nutmeg, and cook over high heat, stirring, until the liquid evaporates. Then slowly add the stock, about ½ cup at a time, stirring each time you add more liquid, and cooking until the liquid is absorbed.

❸ When the rice is *al dente*, stir in the cream, if using, and warm through.

❹ Stir in the Parmesan cheese, then serve immediately, garnished with basil. Offer extra Parmesan for people to help themselves.

grains

Red wine risotto with mushrooms and sausage

Risotto con Funghi e Salsiccia There is lots of room for creativity here, or for practicality—the risotto will be delicious whichever type of sausage you choose.

SERVES 4

- ½ oz dried porcini, about 6 large slices
- ½ cup water
- 4 Tbsp butter
- 5 shallots, chopped
- 3 garlic cloves, chopped
- 1 Italian, anise- or fennel-flavored sausage
- 4 oz common cultivated mushrooms, diced
- 1½ cups Arborio rice
- 2 fresh ripe or canned tomatoes, finely diced
- ¾ cup red wine
- 1 pinch each rosemary, thyme, and savory
- 3 cups hot stock
- freshly shredded Parmesan

Preparation: 30-40 minutes

Cooking time : 40 minutes

❶ Place the porcini and water in a saucepan. Bring to a boil, then simmer until tender. Leave to cool, then squeeze dry, saving the liquid. Roughly chop and set aside. Strain the liquid and set aside.

❷ Melt butter and sauté shallots and garlic until softened, then stir in the sausage and diced mushrooms. Cook until lightly browned. Add the rice and cook for 5–10 minutes, or until golden.

❸ Add the tomatoes, wine, and herbs, then cook, stirring, until the moisture has evaporated. Stir in the mushroom liquid, then the stock, little by little, letting the rice absorb the liquid as you go (about 40 minutes).

❹ When the rice is *al dente*, stir in the mushrooms, warm through, then stir in a few spoonfuls of Parmesan cheese, adjusting for taste.

Grains

Couscous with Wild Mushrooms

Though it's easy to think of couscous as the base for a lusty spicy vegetable or meat feast, it is equally delicious as a side dish. It pairs surprisingly well with wild mushrooms of all types, a fact not lost on North Africans when they are so lucky as to find a cache of mushrooms.

SERVES 4

• 3–4 Tbsp mixed dried mushrooms
• 4 cups vegetable stock or mushroom liquid if on hand
• 3–5 shallots or 1 onion, chopped
• 5 garlic cloves, chopped
• 3–4 Tbsp butter
• several pinches whole cumin seeds
• a small grating of nutmeg
• 2 cups instant couscous
• 4–6 oz Jarlsberg or Gruyère cheese, shredded
• salt and ground black pepper, to taste

Preparation: 25-30 minutes
Cooking time : 10-15 minutes

❶ Combine the dried mushrooms with the stock or mushroom liquid, and bring to a boil. Reduce the heat and simmer 15 minutes, or until softened. Remove from the heat. When cool enough to handle, squeeze the mushrooms, saving all the liquid, then roughly chop, and set aside.

❷ Strain the mushroom liquid, return it to the saucepan, and cook over high heat until reduced by about one third.

❸ Meanwhile, lightly sauté the shallots or onion and garlic in two thirds of the butter until softened, then add the mushrooms, and cook a few minutes more, until the mixture is golden brown. Season with the cumin and nutmeg.

❹ Pour the couscous into the boiling mushroom liquid and cook on low heat, stirring, for just a few minutes, or until the couscous absorbs the liquid. You do not want it to become mushy. Cover for a minute or two to plump up, then uncover, and toss in the sautéed mushrooms, the remaining butter, and the cheese. Season with salt and pepper, and serve immediately.

grains

Mushrooms of all types are superb cooked on the open fire of the broiler or barbecue. The first time I tasted this method of cooking was predictably with porcini, broiled and drizzled with olive oil, as big as the plate and as satisfying as a steak. I've since then discovered that most mushrooms are terrific cooked on the fire, even plain ordinary cultivated ones. And if your mushrooms are too small to sit on top of the grid, skewer them, and then barbecue them.

barbecuing & broiling

Barbecued Steak

and Shiitake Mushrooms with Red Chili-garlic Butter

Cooking mushrooms on the barbecue creates the perfect accompaniment to big juicy steaks cooked outdoors. The earthy, smoky scent of the fire perfumes the fungi with its enticing aroma and flavor.

SERVES 4

- 12 large shiitake mushrooms
- 4–5 Tbsp olive oil
- 8 garlic cloves, chopped
- 2 Tbsp lemon juice
- salt and ground black pepper, to taste
- 1 tsp chopped fresh thyme
- 2½ lb fillet or fillet tail steak
- 3 Tbsp red wine

For the Red Chili-garlic Butter

- 3 oz sweet butter, softened
- 3–4 garlic cloves, chopped
- 1 tsp mild red chili powder, or more to taste
- 1 tsp paprika
- ¼ tsp ground cumin, or to taste
- ½ tsp oregano or thyme leaves, crushed or chopped
- juice of ¼ lime or lemon
- salt, to taste

Preparation: 40-45 minutes
Cooking time : 10-15 minutes

❶ Marinate the mushrooms in half the olive oil, half the garlic, the lemon juice, some salt, and half the thyme. Toss the steak in the remaining olive oil, garlic, and thyme, and add the red wine. Leave both to marinate while you start the barbecue, for at least 30 minutes.

❷ Cook the steak and mushrooms on the barbecue or under a broiler. If the shiitakes are too small to fit on the grid of the barbecue, and threaten to fall through, skewer them with soaked bamboo sticks or with metal skewers. Alternatively, use the broiler.

❸ Combine the ingredients for red chili-garlic butter and mix well. Set aside.

❹ Barbecue the steak for about 8 minutes on each side for rare to medium rare, then remove from the barbecue, and place on a board. Keep warm while you barbecue the mushrooms. This rest will relax the fibers of the meat for a more tender dish.

❺ Cook the mushrooms for about 3 minutes on each side until juicy inside and nicely browned outside.

❻ Slice the steak about ¾ inch against the grain, and serve each portion of steak together with several mushrooms, and a dollop of red chili-garlic butter slathered on both steak and mushrooms, melting deliciously into a buttery sauce.

Kebabs of Shiitake Mushrooms, Tofu, and Onion

This makes a good appetizer or a vegetarian main course served on a pile of Far Eastern rice pilaf. Sometimes I serve it with a spicy peanut sauce for dipping. It's delicious served at room temperature, too, so toss some on the barbecue when you are having a cook-out, and enjoy them at room temperature as an appetizer the next day.

SERVES 4

- 6–8 fresh shiitake mushrooms, quartered
- 12 oz tofu, cut into bite-size chunks
- 3–4 onions, cut into bite-size chunks
- 5 garlic cloves, chopped
- 3–5 Tbsp soy sauce
- 1 Tbsp lime or lemon juice
- several shakes of Tabasco sauce
- 2 Tbsp sesame oil
- ½ tsp ground cumin
- ¼ tsp ground coriander
- 1 Tbsp shredded or finely chopped fresh ginger root
- several pinches Chinese five-spice powder
- 3 Tbsp vegetable oil
- bamboo skewers

Preparation: 40-45 minutes

Cooking time : 5-10 minutes

❶ Place the shiitakes, tofu, and onions in a shallow, non-metallic pan and sprinkle with the remaining ingredients, turning everything so that it is all coated. Leave to marinate for at least 30 minutes and preferably overnight, turning several times.

❷ Soak the skewers in cold water for 30 minutes; this helps keep them from burning.

❸ Thread the shiitake, tofu, and onion onto each skewer, then cook over medium heat on the barbecue. Serve hot or at room temperature.

Barbecued Portobellos

Be sure to marinate the portobellos for that extra dimension. Olive oil, lemon juice or balsamic or sherry vinegar, and lots of garlic or shallots, make the best marinade, boosted with fresh thyme, tarragon, or parsley.

SERVES 4

- 2 big portobellos as a side dish, 4 as a main course
- 3–5 garlic cloves, chopped
- 2–3 Tbsp olive oil
- juice of ½ lemon or 1 Tbsp sherry or balsamic vinegar
- salt, ground black pepper, and thyme, to taste

Preparation: 25-40 minutes

Cooking time : 10 minutes

❶ Sprinkle the mushrooms with the garlic, olive oil, lemon juice or vinegar, and seasonings. Leave for 15–30 minutes.

❷ Cook on the barbecue, preferably a kettle-topped one that lets you cover it, ensuring the food is surrounded by hot, smoky heat. Turn once or twice, letting the mushrooms cook until lightly browned but juicy inside.

❸ Serve immediately, whole or sliced.

▲ *Kebabs of Shiitake Mushrooms, Tofu, and Onion*

Barbecued duck breasts and porcini

Magret aux Porcini Grillé au Feu de Bois *The southwest of France is known for its dishes with duck, and for its abundance of fungi, eaten in simple dishes such as the following one of grilled boneless duck breast and tasty foresty porcini. Begin the meal with a rustic French vegetable soup, drink a delicious Paulliac or Gaillac, and follow with a plate of delectable greens and a selection of glorious French cheeses.*

SERVES 4

- 4 half magrets (boned duck breasts)
- salt and ground black pepper, to taste
- ¼ cup red wine
- 5 garlic cloves, chopped
- 3 Tbsp olive oil
- 1½ lb porcini (or other large mushrooms)
- 2 Tbsp chopped fresh parsley

Preparation: 15 minutes

Cooking time : 15 minutes

❶ Score the skin of the magrets evenly, then place in a bowl, and toss with salt, pepper, about half the wine, garlic, and olive oil. Leave for at least an hour, while you prepare the barbecue.

❷ Toss the mushrooms with the remaining wine, garlic, olive oil, and some salt and pepper. These do not need to marinate long—a few minutes is fine.

❸ Cook the duck breasts and mushrooms over the fire, letting the fat cook off of the duck skin, then crisping up, but keeping the duck as rare as possible. Do this by cooking the skin side over a high heat, then the other side very quickly. It should only take about 5 minutes for the skin side, then a minute or two on the other.

❹ Cook the mushrooms a few minutes on each side, then serve the duck breasts cut thinly crosswise (otherwise they tend to be tough) with the mushrooms, all sprinkled with parsley.

VARIATION:

Toulouse Sausages
with Porcini
Use meaty Toulouse sausages, small French sausages made from coarsely chopped pork flavored with wine, garlic, and seasonings, in place of the duck breasts.

As marvelous as mushrooms are with meats, fish poultry, and pasta, they are unsurpassed when eaten on their own or with whatever vegetable the season has to offer. Whether sautéed, gratinéed, simmered, chopped, stewed, or grilled, the foresty flavor and scent of mushrooms adds its own special character and personality to your meal.

A bowl of stewed mushrooms – porcini, mousserons, trompettes de la mort, oyster, shiitakes, morels, enoki, even the simple cultivated ones – perfumed with a whiff of garlic and served with generous amounts of butter, their juices soaked up with hunks of crusty peasant bread; what could be a simpler, or more excellent feast?

vegetable dishes

"Lasagne" of Potatoes

and Oyster and Shiitake Mushrooms

Use any type of mushrooms you desire—the finished dish will taste of whichever you choose. If no fresh wild mushrooms are available, this is a fine dish to use ordinary white or brown mushrooms combined with dried mushrooms such as porcini, mixed mushrooms, trompettes de la mort.

SERVES 4

- 4 large baking potatoes, peeled
- 12 oz fresh oyster and shiitake mushrooms
- 6 Tbsp butter
- salt and black or cayenne pepper, to taste
- 1 Tbsp chopped fresh parsley or chervil, plus extra to serve
- 3 Tbsp chopped fresh tarragon, plus extra to serve
- 2 Tbsp flour
- 2½ cups milk
- several scrapings of nutmeg
- 5–7 Tbsp shredded Parmesan cheese

Preparation: 30 minutes

Cooking time : 1 hour

❶ Parboil the potatoes in salted water until the potatoes' starch has just stabilized but they are still too crunchy to eat. This should take about 15 minutes at a gentle rolling simmer. Let cool in the water then remove and slice thinly. They will be sticky at this point—don't worry.

❷ Preheat a 375°F oven. Sauté the mushrooms quickly and lightly in 4 tablespoons of the butter until slightly browned and golden in places. Sprinkle with salt, pepper, parsley or chervil, and tarragon. Set aside.

❸ Make a béchamel sauce. Heat the remaining butter until melted then sprinkle in the flour. Let heat until lightly golden, then remove from the heat. Meanwhile, heat the milk until bubbles form around the edge of the pan. Pour the milk into the flour mixture, return to the heat, and stir until thickened.

Season with nutmeg, salt, and black or cayenne pepper.

❹ Layer half the sliced potatoes in a buttered gratin or baking pan, cover with half the sautéed mushrooms, then with half the béchamel, then half the Parmesan cheese. Repeat, ending with the Parmesan cheese.

❺ Bake in the oven for 30–40 minutes, or until the potatoes are cooked through and the top of the "lasagne" is light golden. Serve hot with additional chopped tarragon and a little parsley or chervil.

Sauté of Chanterelles

with a Crown of Crispy Potatoes

This dish is very good, too, with a combination of mushrooms. Visit any countryside market in the early fall, and you will be faced with glorious abundance of fungi to choose from. They are not cheap, but they are thrilling, and well worth the expense.

SERVES 4

- 3–4 large baking potatoes, peeled, soaked a few minutes in cold water, then dried and very thinly sliced
- olive oil or melted butter, for brushing
- 1 lb chanterelles, cut into bite-size pieces
- 5 shallots, chopped
- 8 garlic cloves, chopped
- 3–5 Tbsp chopped fresh parsley
- 4 Tbsp sweet butter
- salt and ground black pepper, to taste
- a grating of nutmeg
- ½ cup each red wine and vegetable or chicken stock

Preparation: 20-30 minutes

Cooking time : 20-30 minutes

❶ Preheat a 375°F oven. On a nonstick baking sheet, arrange four rounds, or concentric rings, of the potato slices, letting them stick together with their own juices. Brush with olive oil or melted butter, and bake in the oven until golden and crisply edged, about 25 minutes. They should stick together into their round shapes but if they fall apart when you place them on top of the mushrooms, it doesn't really matter.

❷ While the potatoes bake, sauté the mushrooms with half the shallots, half the garlic, and half the parsley in about 2 tablespoons of the butter. Cook until lightly browned. Season with salt, pepper, and nutmeg, then remove from the pan. Pour in the wine and stock, and boil down to a rich reduced essence of just a few tablespoons. Take care it does not overcook and turn bitter, however.

❸ Remove from the heat, swirl in the remaining butter, then return the mushrooms to the pan and toss with the sauce.

❹ Combine the remaining shallots, garlic, and parsley in a small bowl. Serve each portion of mushrooms on a plate, topped with the potato "crown," with the shallot-garlic-parsley mixture scattered over.

vegetable dishes

103

Stir-fried Mushrooms

with Zucchini and Onions

Serve these flavorful vegetables with steamed jasmine rice, or on a bed of crispy noodles as chow mein.

SERVES 4
- 3 onions, cut into bite-size chunks
- 2–3 Tbsp vegetable oil
- 5 garlic cloves, chopped
- 1–2 Tbsp roughly chopped fresh ginger root
- 2 zucchini, sliced diagonally
- 8–10 oz common cultivated or button mushrooms, quartered
- ½ stock cube, crumbled
- ⅓–½ cup water
- 1½–2 tsp cornstarch mixed with 2–3 Tbsp cold water
- 2 tsp soy sauce, or to taste
- 2 Tbsp chopped fresh cilantro

Preparation: 10-15 minutes
Cooking time : 10-15 minutes

❶ Stir-fry the onions with a tiny amount of the oil over medium-high heat for just a moment, to lightly char rather than cook the onion. Add half the garlic and ginger, then the zucchini, and cook a few moments more, or until the zucchini are crisp yet tender. Remove from the pan.

❷ Add the remaining oil and stir-fry the mushrooms, adding the remaining garlic and ginger. Cook only for a few moments—they should remain crisp and fresh-looking, but be lightly browned in spots—then sprinkle in the stock cube and return the onions and zucchini to the pan.

❸ Gradually stir in the water and the cornstarch paste (you may not need it all), cook a few moments, stir-frying, until the liquid thickens, then season with soy sauce. Serve immediately, with the cilantro scattered over.

vegetable dishes

104

Stir-fry of Black Mushrooms

with Tofu and Green Vegetables

This gentle, nourishing stir-fry combines protein-rich tofu with hearty black mushrooms and crisp, vibrant greens. It is one of my favorite dishes, one that I make whenever that call for comfort arises. Brown rice, with its earthy whole-grain flavor, makes an excellent accompaniment.

SERVES 4

- 8–10 dried shiitake or Chinese black mushrooms
- 1 oz dried black tree cloud fungus
- 1½ cups hot, but not boiling, water
- 11–12 oz firm tofu
- 1 Tbsp cornstarch, plus extra for dusting
- oil, for frying
- 2 carrots, thinly sliced diagonally
- 1 onion, thinly sliced lengthwise
- 3–4 garlic cloves, chopped
- 2–3 Tbsp chopped fresh ginger root
- a large pinch or two of sugar
- 1 small bunch broccoli, cut into florets
- a handful of snow peass, topped and tailed
- ½ cup hot chicken or vegetable stock
- 1 Tbsp soy sauce, or to taste
- 1 Tbsp sesame oil
- 1–2 Tbsp chopped fresh cilantro

Preparation: 45-50 minutes

Cooking time : 15-20 minutes

❶ Rehydrate the shiitake or black mushrooms and tree cloud fungus by placing them in a saucepan with the hot water. Cover and let stand for 30 minutes. If they remain tough, bring the mushrooms, fungus, and liquid to a boil, simmer a few minutes, then remove from the heat. Let stand, covered, as before.

❷ Remove from the pan, strain the mushroom liquid, and reserve. If the tree cloud fungus is in large pieces, cut into bite-size ones. Leave the black mushrooms whole, or halve if they are very large. Set aside.

❸ Cut the tofu into bite-sized cubes, then dry well. Toss with cornstarch to coat. Heat about 3 inches of vegetable oil in a wok or deep frying pan. The oil is hot enough when a cube of bread sizzles and turns golden when dropped in. Carefully slip in the tofu cubes and cook until golden. They will spit, so beware. The cooking will take at least 5 minutes. Turn them occasionally and keep a close watch. They are at

their most delicious when golden and crisp on the outside and tender inside. When cooked, remove with a slotted spoon, and let drain on paper towels.

❹ Pour off all the oil except for 1–2 tablespoons. Heat the wok or pan, and stir-fry the carrots, onion, garlic, and ginger. Then sprinkle with sugar, cook a few minutes more, and add the broccoli, reserved black mushrooms and tree cloud fungus, and a tablespoon or two of the mushroom liquid. Cover and cook a moment, then remove the cover, let the liquid evaporate quickly, and add the snow peas.

❺ Mix the stock with an equal amount of the mushroom liquid, soy sauce, and cornstarch. Stir well, then stir this into the mixture, and cook, stirring, until thickened.

❻ Turn onto a platter, drizzle with sesame oil, sprinkle with cilantro. Serve immediately.

Stir-fry of Broccoli

and Black Mushrooms in Hoisin Sauce with Cashews

Florets of crisp-tender, fresh green broccoli and soft, chewy earthy black mushrooms are cloaked in spicy-sweet hoisin sauce, and scattered with whole cashews. Baby corn or water chestnuts would also be good in the mélange.

Delicious as a side dish, as an accompaniment for something simple such as a roasted duck or steamed whole fish, along with a bowl of rice, or enjoy as a main course over wide rice noodles.

SERVES 4

- 10–12 dried Chinese black mushrooms
- 1 onion, thinly sliced lengthwise
- 3 garlic cloves, chopped
- 2 tsp chopped fresh ginger root
- 2 Tbsp vegetable oil, or as needed
- soy sauce, to taste
- 2 bunches broccoli, stems peeled and cut into bite-size pieces, florets broken into bite-size pieces
- 1–2 tsp sugar, or more to taste
- ½ cup stock
- 1–2 tsp cornstarch mixed with 1 Tbsp water
- 1 Tbsp rice wine or sherry
- 4–5 Tbsp hoisin sauce
- a pinch each Chinese five-spice powder and white or cayenne pepper
- 2 oz toasted cashews, preferably dry roasted
- 1 Tbsp chopped fresh cilantro
- ½ tsp sesame oil

Preparation: 25-30 minutes
Cooking time : 10-15 minutes

❶ Rehydrate the mushrooms by placing them in a saucepan with water to cover. Bring to a boil, then reduce the heat, and simmer about 5 minutes. Let stand 10–15 minutes, then remove from the water, and squeeze dry. Cut the stems off, if they are tough, and set aside.

❷ Stir-fry the onion, garlic, and ginger in half the oil, then add the mushrooms, and cook a few moments. Sprinkle with soy sauce, cook a moment, then remove from the pan.

❸ Add the remaining oil, stir-fry the broccoli until it is crisp-tender, sprinkling with about ¼ teaspoon sugar as you stir-fry, then remove the broccoli from the pan.

❹ Add the stock and cornstarch paste, stir until slightly thickened, then add the rice wine or sherry, hoisin sauce, five-spice powder, white or cayenne pepper and the remaining sugar. Cook a few minutes until slightly thickened.

❺ Return the mushrooms and broccoli to the pan, and toss in the cashews. Serve with the cilantro and sesame oil.

vegetable diabes

"Cassoulet" of Porcini and White Beans

Serve it with a salad of mesclum and a scattering of Roquefort. For a double mushroom meal, you might want to sauté a handful of oyster mushrooms and toss them, warm, onto the lightly dressed salad.

SERVES 4
- 1 lb dried white beans, such as cannellini, soaked overnight
- 2 bay leaves
- 2 oz dried porcini or 1 oz dried porcini plus 8 oz fresh
- 1 onion, chopped
- 1 large baking potato, diced
- ½ carrot, diced
- 1 garlic bulb, cloves separated but left whole
- 4–6 Tbsp olive oil, or as needed
- salt and ground black pepper, to taste
- ¼ tsp dried herbes de Provence
- 1½ cups dry white wine
- 2 cups stock
- 2½ cups fresh bread crumbs
- 5 garlic cloves, chopped
- 3 Tbsp chopped fresh parsley

Preparation: 30 minutes

Cooking time : 5 hours

❶ Drain the soaked beans and place in a pan with the bay leaves and water to cover. Bring to a boil, reduce the heat, and simmer over medium-low heat, covered, until tender, about 2 hours. Drain.

❷ Preheat a 325°F oven. Rehydrate the mushrooms in the water by bring it to a boil, then reducing the heat, and simmering a few minutes. Let stand and plump up, then leave to cool. Remove from the water, chop roughly, and set aside. Strain the liquid and set aside.

❸ Sauté the onion, potato, carrot, and whole garlic cloves in about half the olive oil, until the onion is softened and the vegetables are golden. Season with salt, pepper, and herbes de Provence. Pour in the wine, bring to a boil, and cook over high heat, about 10 minutes.

❹ In a heavy casserole layer the beans, mushrooms, vegetables and wine, and stock. Bake in the oven for 1½ hours, about half the time covered, then with the cover removed. The beans should be creamy and tender by then, but not too runny.

❺ Mix the bread crumbs with the chopped garlic and parsley. Spread about half this mixture over the beans, drizzle with half the remaining olive oil, then raise the oven temperature to 400°F, and bake for about 15 minutes. You don't want to burn the crumb topping, so reduce the oven temperature to 375°F if you think there is a danger of this.

❻ With a spoon, break the crust, and stir it into the cassoulet. Top with the remaining crumb mixture and drizzle over the rest of the olive oil, then return to the oven for another 15 minutes. Serve immediately.

Potato and Mushroom Cakes

on a Bed of Mixed Leaves

Mashed potatoes are mixed with sautéed mushrooms, formed into cakes, and fried to a crisp. Serve on a bed of mixed leaves, with a wedge of lemon for squeezing, a mushroom sauce, or a little sour cream on the side, if desired.

SERVES 4

- 1 Tbsp mixed dried mushrooms (optional)
- 12 oz fresh common cultivated or large flat mushrooms, chopped
- 2 onions, chopped
- 3 Tbsp olive oil
- 2 bay leaves
- 3 garlic cloves, chopped
- salt and ground black pepper, to taste
- 4 boiled potatoes, mashed
- 2 eggs, lightly beaten
- 2 Tbsp sour cream or cottage cheese
- 3 Tbsp bread crumbs, plus extra for coating
- olive oil, for frying
- mixed leaves, to serve

Preparation: 25 minutes

Cooking time : 45 minutes

❶ If you are using dried mushrooms, rehydrate by placing in a saucepan with water to cover, and bring to a boil. Reduce the heat and simmer 5–10 minutes. Remove from the heat. Take the mushrooms from the liquid, roughly chop, and set aside.

❷ Sauté all the mushrooms and the onions in the olive oil, with the bay leaves and garlic. When the onions are tender and the mushrooms browned, season with salt and pepper.

❸ In a large bowl, mix the mashed potato, egg, sour cream or cottage cheese, and measured bread crumbs. Add the mushroom mixture, and combine well. Form patties with your hands, and coat each one in bread crumbs.

❹ Chill for at least 30 minutes, then fry in a heavy-based frying pan in ½–1 inch olive oil. Cook until crisp and browned. Keep the cakes warm as they are cooked, and serve on a bed of mixed leaves.

vegetable dishes

Paprikash of Mushrooms

Rich and russet hued from paprika, this is a simple sauté of mushrooms and peppers based on that Hungarian stew of meat or vegetables simmered with paprika and enriched with heavy or sour cream.

Serve with spaetzel, or noodles, or even Rumanian-style, over a mound of soft polenta.

SERVES 4

- 2 onions, chopped
- 5 garlic cloves, chopped
- 3–5 Tbsp butter, or less if desired
- 1 lb firm button, common cultivated white, or brown mushrooms, quartered
- ½ each fresh red and green pepper, diced
- 3–5 small fresh ripe tomatoes or about 6 oz canned, diced
- 1–2 Tbsp flour
- 2–3 tsp paprika, or more if desired
- ¼ tsp fresh thyme
- ½ cup dry white wine
- ½ cup stock
- 1 cup crème fraîche, or half ricotta cheese, half heavy or light cream
- salt and ground black pepper, to taste
- 3–5 scallions, chopped, to garnish

Preparation: 10-15 minutes
Cooking time : 15-30 minutes

❶ Lightly sauté the onion and garlic in about half the butter until softened, then remove from the pan, and set aside. Add the remaining butter to the pan. Sauté the mushrooms, then remove, and set aside. In the same pan, cook the red and green peppers and tomatoes a few moments, until softened a little. Sprinkle in the flour, cook a few minutes, then sprinkle in the paprika and thyme, and cook together for several minutes, taking care that the paprika does not burn.

❷ Return the onions and mushrooms to the pan, along with the wine and stock, and simmer for 15 minutes, until the vegetables are cooked. Stir the crème fraîche, or ricotta cheese mixture, season with salt and pepper, and warm through over gentle heat. Taste for seasoning and serve immediately, with the scallions scattered over.

Gratin of Potatoes and Trompettes de la Mort

Gratin aux Pommes de Terre et Trompettes de la Mort *This exquisite gratin is a culinary souvenir from a winter stay in France's Jura. The mushrooms were pulled out of a huge jar, having been foraged for then dried the previous fall.*

SERVES 4

- 2 oz trompettes de la mort
- 1 cup stock or water
- 8 baking potatoes (about 2½ lb in total)
- ½ cup butter
- salt and ground black pepper, to taste
- 10 shallots, chopped or sliced
- 8–10 garlic cloves, chopped
- 1½ cups light cream
- 2 cups shredded Parmesan, comte, fontina, or Gruyère cheese, or a combination, for sprinkling
- 1 Tbsp pink peppercorns
- 2 Tbsp chopped fresh parsley

Preparation: 50 minutes

Cooking time : 40 minutes

vegetable diabes

❶ Place the mushrooms in a saucepan with the stock or water and bring to a boil. Reduce the heat, simmer for 5–10 minutes, or until the mushrooms are tender, then remove from the heat. When mushrooms are cool enough to handle, remove from the saucepan, and set aside. Strain the mushroom liquid and set aside.

❷ Peel and thinly slice the potatoes, and place them in cold water to cover. Leave for about 30 minutes, then drain, and dry well. I like to use a clean dish towel and lay the potatoes in it, patting them all dry.

❸ Preheat a 375°F oven. Butter the base of a gratin pan and make a layer of the potatoes on the base. Sprinkle with salt, pepper, shallots, and garlic, and add some little dots of butter, then make another layer of potatoes. Every so often make a layer of the mushrooms. End with the potatoes, dotted with a tablespoon or so of the butter.

❹ Pour the reserved mushroom liquid over the potatoes, then pour the cream over and finally sprinkle with the cheese. Bake in the oven for about an hour, or until the top is crusty and browned and the potatoes are meltingly tender.

❺ Serve sprinkled with pink peppercorns and parsley.

Roasted Oyster Mushrooms

with Tender Whole Garlic Cloves

Blanching whole unpeeled garlic cloves makes them tender and sweet. Any kind of oyster mushrooms are delicious, and a selection is quite fun, as you can discover the different qualities of each type in one dish. Or you might choose a selection of different mushrooms altogether. The mushrooms and poached garlic can be sautéed in a large heavy-based frying pan, in several batches, if needed, so as not to crowd the mushrooms.

SERVES 4

- 2 garlic bulbs, cloves separated but unpeeled
- 2 cups vegetable or chicken stock
- 1 lb oyster mushrooms, whole but broken into clumps
- 6 Tbsp butter or olive oil, or as desired
- 2 garlic cloves, chopped
- several sprigs fresh thyme
- 1 Tbsp chopped fresh parsley or snipped fresh chives

Preparation: 10-15 minutes

Cooking time : 50 minutes

❶ Preheat a 350°F oven. Simmer the whole garlic cloves in the stock until almost tender and the liquid has reduced by about half, about 10 minutes.

❷ Place the mushrooms in a roasting pan. Surround with the garlic cloves and drizzle with the stock. Stud the top of the mushrooms and the garlic cloves with the butter or drizzle with the olive oil, sprinkle with chopped garlic and thyme, then roast for 20–30 minutes. If they are not done, raise the oven temperature to 375°–400°F, and roast for 5–10 minutes more.

❸ Serve sprinkled with parsley or chives.

TIP:

Don't throw out the garlic poaching liquid. It is great for making soups or for adding to vegetable or meat stocks.

vegetable dishes

Mushrooms Afelia-style

Manitaria Afelia *Afelia-style is a particular Cypriot style of cooking involving stewing foods in red wine with coriander seeds. Serve as part of the parade of little dishes that makes up a meze dinner, or as a hot appetizer, accompanied by crusty bread.*

vegetable dishes

SERVES 4 AS AN APPETIZER, SIDE DISH, OR SEPARATE VEGETABLE COURSE

- 1–2 Tbsp each olive oil and butter
- 1 onion, chopped
- 4 garlic cloves, roughly chopped
- 1 lb fairly small button mushrooms, quartered
- 1 cup red wine
- 1 cup beef or vegetable stock
- 1 Tbsp coarsely crushed coriander seeds
- a pinch of ground cumin
- salt and ground black pepper, to taste
- a squeeze of lemon juice

Preparation: 10 minutes

Cooking time : 20 minutes

❶ Melt the olive oil and butter together over low heat in a large, heavy-based sauté or frying pan, add the onion, and gently sauté until softened.

❷ Add the garlic and mushrooms, and sauté over medium-high heat until the mushrooms are lightly browned—you may need to do this in several batches so that they brown and do not become watery. As they are cooked, remove the mushrooms, with the onion, to a plate.

❸ Pour the wine and stock into the pan, with the coriander seeds and cumin. Bring to a boil and cook over high heat until reduced to about ½–⅔ cup.

❹ Return the mushrooms and onion (and any juices that have accumulated) to the pan. Cook over high heat about 5 minutes, or until the mushrooms are tender. Season with salt, pepper, and a squeeze of lemon juice. Serve immediately.

Garlicky Mashed Potatoes

with Wild Mushrooms

Rich and wintery, this makes a comforting dish to enjoy on a chilly night either alongside a meaty main course, or as its own course, served in a bowl and eaten with a spoon.

SERVES 4

- 8 oz fresh mushrooms or ½ oz mixed dried mushrooms, or all porcini
- ½ cup water, if using dried mushrooms
- 4 baking potatoes, cut into chunks
- 10 garlic cloves, 5 whole, 5 chopped
- 4 Tbsp olive oil
- 2 Tbsp mushroom jus (see page 127) or brandy, if using fresh mushrooms
- ½ cup light cream
- salt and ground black pepper, to taste
- 3–5 Tbsp snipped fresh chives

Preparation: 20 minutes

Cooking time : 30 minutes

❶ If using fresh mushrooms, chop them roughly. If using dried mushrooms, rehydrate by placing in a saucepan with the water, bringing to a boil, then reducing the heat, and simmering for about 5 minutes. Leave the mushrooms to cool at least 15 minutes, then remove from the water. Squeeze dry, roughly chop, and set aside. Strain the mushroom liquid, then bring to a boil, and reduce to 2 tablespoons.

❷ Meanwhile, cook the potatoes together with the whole garlic cloves in lightly salted water to cover. When tender, drain, and mash.

❸ Heat the olive oil in a frying pan, and toss in the chopped garlic and the mushrooms. Warm through, then add the 2 tablespoons mushroom jus, brandy, or reduced mushroom liquid, and cook down until evaporated.

❹ Mix this into the mashed potatoes, along with the cream, salt and pepper, and chives. Taste for seasoning, and serve with the addition of a nugget of butter to melt on top, if you like.

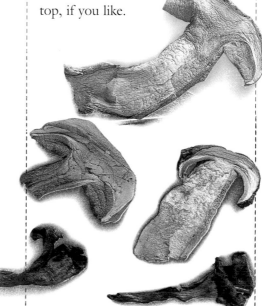

Spanish Roasted Mushrooms

This simple Mediterranean dish of roasted mushrooms is sprinkled with fino sherry, garlic, and butter, with a scattering of almonds, which toast while the mushrooms cook.

SERVES 4

- 1 lb large flat mushrooms
- 1 Tbsp fino sherry
- 5 garlic cloves, chopped
- 3 Tbsp butter
- 1 Tbsp chopped fresh parsley
- salt and ground black pepper, to taste
- 3–4 Tbsp slivered almonds

Preparation: 10 minutes

Cooking time : 20 minutes

❶ Preheat a 400°F oven. Arrange the mushrooms on a large baking sheet and sprinkle the sherry, then the garlic, over the top. Dot with the butter, sprinkle with parsley, salt, pepper, and almonds.

❷ Bake in the oven until the mushrooms sizzle and the nuts are toasted, about 20 minutes. Serve immediately.

Tender White Beans with Mixed Mushrooms,

Wine, Tomatoes, and Eggplant

Haricots aux Champignons et Aubergine *This stewy mélange, with its earthy scent of mushrooms, hearty beans, and meaty eggplant, is decidedly appetizing. Serve it in a rustic ceramic casserole, accompanied by crusty bread for dipping into, and follow with a countryside salad of Belgian endive and herbs, and perhaps a slab or two of Roquefort.*

SERVES 4

- 8 oz dried white beans, soaked overnight
- 2 bay leaves
- 3–4 Tbsp mixed dried mushrooms, such as forest mix containing porcini, trompettes de la mort, and morels or mousserons
- 1 medium-large onion, chopped
- 5 garlic cloves, roughly chopped
- 1/3–1/2 cup extra virgin olive oil, plus extra if needed and to finish
- 12–14 oz fresh ripe tomatoes or canned with their juice, diced
- 1 1/2 cups red wine
- several sprigs of fresh thyme
- salt and ground black pepper, to taste
- a pinch of sugar, or to taste
- 1 smallish eggplant, cut into bite-size pieces
- chopped fresh parsley, to garnish

Preparation: 20-25 minutes

Cooking time : 1½ hours

❶ Place the soaked beans and bay leaves in a saucepan, with fresh water to cover. Bring to a boil, then reduce the heat, and cook over medium-low heat until the beans are ready, about 1 hour, depending on the bean you use. (Check the instructions on the package.)

❷ A half hour before the beans will be cooked through, add the dried mushrooms. Cook until the beans are tender and the mushrooms rehydrated. Spoon the beans and mushrooms from the pot and place in a bowl. Strain the liquid, and set aside.

❸ Meanwhile, sauté the onion and half the garlic in a few tablespoons of the olive oil and, when softened, add the tomatoes. Cook over medium-high heat until saucelike, then add the wine and thyme. Cook over medium-high heat until the wine has nearly evaporated. Adjust seasoning, and add sugar to taste. Then set aside.

❹ Brown the eggplant in the remaining olive oil, adding extra if needed. When tender but browned, remove from the pan.

❺ In a frying pan, combine the beans and mushrooms with the tomato mixture, eggplant, and the beans and strained mushroom liquid. Cook over high heat, stirring occasionally but gently so as not to break up the beans, until the liquid is reduced to a reasonable amount. Season with salt, and stir in a bit of extra olive oil to taste. Serve garnished with chopped fresh parsley.

TIP:

Choose any white bean you like. Although butter beans taste lovely, they tend to go mushy, and fall apart. I go for Greek fasoulia gigantes, French lingots, or Italian cannellini.

vegetable dishes

Whether eaten as an appetizer, cut into small pieces as antipasti, or enjoyed as a mid-afternoon snack or supper, pizza, savory tarts, and zesty mixtures—either spooned onto bread or rolled into tortillas—are the perfect vehicle for the versatile mushroom.

pizzas & bread dishes

Wild and tamed mushrooms are all delicious, either on their own or in conjunction with each other. And the dishes that follow range from unashamedly luxurious—such as Pizza with Porcini and Truffles (see page 119), which is packed with porcini and truffles—to down to earth. Enjoy!

Marsala-scented Mushrooms on Crisp Toasts

Crostini alla Funghi *This makes a marvelous spuntino, or little afternoon snack, with a glass of wine to wash it down.*

SERVES 4

- 4 Tbsp butter
- 1 onion, finely chopped
- 3–4 garlic cloves, chopped
- 12 oz mixed fresh mushrooms, such as porcini, ordinary white or black mushrooms, oyster mushrooms, chanterelles, trompettes de mort, and shiitakes, dried or roughly chopped
- 2–3 Tbsp Marsala
- several gratings of nutmeg
- 3 Tbsp heavy cream
- 5 Tbsp fromage frais or ricotta cheese
- 3–5 Tbsp freshly shredded Parmesan cheese
- salt and ground black pepper, to taste
- 8–12 slices of baguette or tight-crumbed bread, cut into fingers

Preparation: 10-15 minutes
Cooking time : 20-25 minutes

❶ Melt the butter, then sauté the onion, garlic, and mushrooms together until lightly browned. Pour in the Marsala, and evaporate over high heat.

❷ Remove from the heat and add the nutmeg, cream, fromage frais or ricotta cheese, and Parmesan. Season with salt and pepper.

❸ Lightly toast both sides of the bread, then spread one side with the cheese mixture. Broil until lightly browned on top, then serve hot.

pizzas, and bread dishes

Basic Pizza Dough

The pizza is a wonderfully versatile dish, allowing for great creativity in devising different toppings.

Use this dough recipe for your pizza and calzone bases. The water should be at body temperature; test it against the back of your wrist.

MAKES 1 12-INCH ROUND PIZZA

- 3 cups all-purpose flour
- ½ tsp salt
- 1 envelope active dry yeast
- a pinch of sugar
- about 1 cup warm water
- ⅓ cup olive oil

**Rising time : 1-1½ hours
at room temperature
Cooking time : 15-25 minutes**

❶ Preheat a 425°F oven. Sift the flour and stir in the salt, yeast, and sugar. Make a well in the center.

❷ Reserve 3–4 tablespoons of the water, and mix the rest with the oil, then pour it into the well. Using your hands, gradually mix the flour into the liquid, a little at a time, from the sides of the bowl, until the mixture combines to form a soft dough. If it seems too dry, add a little more water.

❸ Turn the dough out onto a lightly floured board and knead for about 10 minutes, or until smooth, elastic, and with a satiny sheen. When you poke your finger in, the dough should spring back out. If it remains too sticky, knead in a bit more flour.

❹ Place the dough in an oiled bowl, cover with a clean dish towel, plastic bag, or plastic wrap, and leave in a warm place until doubled in size. An airing cupboard or warm kitchen will make for quicker rising—about 1–1½ hours. (If you would like to make the dough ahead of time, let it rise a day or two in the fridge, taking care that it is loosely wrapped to allow for expansion.)

❺ Punch the dough down, then leave to rise again. This time will be a lot quicker. (Again, you can do this in the fridge to suit your timing.)

❻ When ready to make your pizza, roll out the dough to fit a 12-inch, round, lightly oiled pizza pan, or place on a lightly oiled baking sheet, pressing the dough to form a slightly raised edge. Add your chosen topping.

❼ Bake in the oven for about 15–20 minutes, or until golden brown.

pizzas and bread dishes

Pizza with Porcini and Truffles

Pizza ai Porcini e Tartuffe *Mushrooms and delicate mozzarella cheese make a lovely combination. Using them to top a pizza, combined with a heady dose of truffle, is a specialty of Norcia, the Umbrian town as famous in Italy for its truffles as the Périgord is in France.*

SERVES 4

- 1 quantity Basic Pizza Dough (see opposite)
- 3 oz dried porcini
- 1 large black flat mushroom or 8 oz fresh mushrooms, such as chanterelles, trompettes de mort, or porcini
- 3 Tbsp olive oil
- salt and ground black pepper, to taste
- 3 garlic cloves, chopped
- 12 oz mozzarella cheese, coarsely shredded
- 1 oz truffle/porcini or truffle condiment
- 3–4 Tbsp freshly shredded Parmesan or pecorino cheese
- a few drops of truffle oil, to serve (optional)

Preparation (excluding dough time) : 15 minutes
Cooking time : 25 minutes

❶ Roll out the dough and use to line an oiled pizza pan or four individual pans. Set aside.

❷ Rehydrate the dried mushrooms by placing them in a pan with water to cover and simmering until tender, about 10 minutes. Remove from the heat and, when cool enough to handle, squeeze dry.

❸ Preheat a 400°F oven. Lightly sauté the rehydrated and fresh mushrooms in the olive oil, until the fresh mushrooms are wilted and soft. Add salt, pepper, and the garlic, Leave to cool.

❹ Spread half the cheese over the pizza base(s). Top with the mushrooms, add dollops of the truffle/porcini or truffle condiment, another layer of mozzarella cheese, and a sprinkling of Parmesan or pecorino.

❺ Bake in the oven for 20–25 minutes, or until the topping is melted and sizzling, and the dough bubbly and cooked through. Serve immediately, with a few drops of truffle oil, if desired.

119

Tomato and Mushroom Pizza

Pizza ai Funghi e Pomadori *Tomatoes and mushrooms have a natural affinity. This pizza topping creates a wonderfully deep and rich flavor, which is lifted by the inclusion of fresh oregano.*

SERVES 4

- 1 quantity Basic Pizza Dough (see page 118)
- 4 Tbsp tomato paste (optional)
- ½ cup passata
- 2–3 fresh ripe or canned tomatoes, diced
- 2 garlic cloves, chopped
- 1 tsp fresh oregano, crumbled
- 8 oz common cultivated mushrooms, white or brown, thinly sliced
- 12 oz mozzarella cheese, or half mozzarella, half fontina, shredded
- 2 Tbsp olive oil
- freshly shredded Parmesan cheese, to taste

Preparation: 10 minutes

Cooking time : 20 minutes

❶ Preheat a 400°F oven. Roll out the dough and use to line an oiled pizza pan. Spread the dough with the tomato paste, if using, then drizzle with the passata.

❷ Scatter the tomatoes, garlic, oregano, mushrooms, and mozzarella cheese, or mozzarella and fontina cheeses, over the top. Drizzle with the olive oil, and sprinkle with as much Parmesan cheese as you like.

❸ Bake in the oven for 15–20 minutes, or until the cheeses have melted and turned golden in spots, and the crust is golden and its edges have risen.

Sautéed Mixed Mushrooms with Rosemary

Focaccio, Goat Cheese, and Mozzarella Cheese

Bruschetta di Funghi Misti con Pane Rosemarino e Due Formaggio *Quick and easy to prepare, these bruschetta make a flavorful lunchtime treat, especially when washed down with a glass of robust red wine.*

SERVES 4

- 1 lb mixed fresh exotic mushrooms, roughly chopped
- 4 garlic cloves, chopped
- 4–6 Tbsp olive oil
- salt and ground black pepper, to taste
- chopped fresh rosemary, to taste
- 4 slices focaccio
- 1 garlic clove, halved
- 4 oz goat cheese, thinly sliced
- 4 oz mozzarella cheese, thinly sliced
- 3 Tbsp chopped fresh parsley

Preparation: 20 minutes

Cooking time : 20 minutes

❶ Lightly sauté the mushrooms and garlic in a heavy-based frying pan in the olive oil, until the mushrooms are lightly browned. Season with salt, pepper, and rosemary, and set aside.

❷ Lightly toast the bottom of the focaccio slices, then turn them over and rub the tops with the halved garlic clove. Top each slice with a layer of goat cheese and another of mozzarella cheese.

❸ Broil the bruschetta until the cheeses melt. Meanwhile heat the mushrooms, tossing, until they are quite hot. Serve the cheese-topped toasts immediately, with the mushroom mixture spooned over, and sprinkled with chopped parsley.

Wild Mushroom Quesadillas

Quesadillas are no more than melted cheese sandwiches, Mexican-style, made on a flat corn or flour tortilla instead of on bread. Anything can be added to them: savory stewed and chilied meats are a traditional treat, while vegetarian fillings such as barbecued or broiled vegetables or sautéed wild mushrooms add an innovative, contemporary flair.

SERVES 4

- 1 onion, chopped
- 5 garlic cloves, chopped
- 3–4 Tbsp olive oil
- 8 oz mixed fresh mushrooms, chopped
- a pinch of ground cumin
- salt and ground black pepper, to taste
- 1–2 Tbsp finely chopped fresh cilantro
- 8 smallish fresh corn tortillas
- 3 cups shredded cheese, such as Jack, fontina, mozzarella, asiago, or any mild white cheese that melts well
- bottled hot sauce, to serve

Preparation: 10-15 minutes

Cooking time : 15-20 minutes

❶ Sauté the onion and garlic in the olive oil until softened, then add the mushrooms and cook, turning, until lightly browned and tender. This will depend on the mushrooms you choose. Season with cumin, salt, and pepper, sprinkle with the cilantro, then set aside and keep warm.

❷ To make the quesadillas, warm the tortillas either in a heavy-based, lightly greased frying pan or stack, unwrapped on a plate, and microwave at top heat for about 60 seconds. When they are warm, take each one and sprinkle with cheese. Working one at a time, keep them warm and supple by covering the stack of tortillas not yet being used with a damp kitchen or paper towel. Fold over and heat through again, one at a time, either in the microwave or the frying pan. When the cheese has melted, open the tortilla and stuff some of the mushrooms inside. Serve immediately, with bottled hot sauce. (If you like, place each one as it is made on a baking sheet, cover lightly, and keep warm in a low oven until ready to serve.)

TIP:

Select some flavorful and some milder-tasting mushrooms, such as oysters, chanterelles, trompettes de la mort, and common cultivated.

Morel and Other Mushrooms in Cheese Fondue

Croûtes aux Morilles et Champignons Varis These dreamy mushroom and cheese toasts are so moreish, you may want to make double quantities. The amounts given here would serve double.

SERVES 8

- 1 oz dried morel mushrooms
- 1 cup hot, but not boiling, water
- 6–8 oz mixed fresh mushrooms, such as ordinary button mushrooms, oysters, morels, trompette de la mort, chanterelles, and porcini
- ½ cup dry white wine
- ½ cup vegetable or chicken stock
- 3 cups shredded white cheese, such as comte, Gruyère, Jack, mild white Cheddar, or fontina
- 1 garlic clove, finely chopped
- a few gratings fresh nutmeg
- ¼–⅓ cup heavy cream or crème fraîche
- salt and ground black pepper, to taste
- 8 slices pain levain or other flavorful country bread
- 3–4 Tbsp snipped fresh chives

Preparation: 30 minutes
Cooking time : 15 minutes

❶ Place the dried morels in a bowl and pour over the hot water. Let stand for at least 30 minutes. When cool enough to handle, remove from the liquid, and squeeze dry, saving the liquid. Strain the mushroom liquid, and set aside.

❷ Slice the dried and fresh mushrooms, and combine in a saucepan with the mushroom liquid, wine, and stock. Bring to a boil, then reduce the heat, and simmer for 5–8 minutes, or until the mushrooms are just tender.

❸ Stir in the cheese, garlic, nutmeg, and cream or crème fraîche, cooking over medium-low heat until the cheese melts and the texture is like a fondue. Season with salt and black pepper.

❹ Toast the bread lightly on both sides, then arrange on a baking sheet. Spoon the mushroom mixture over the top. Broil until the tops sizzle slightly, then serve immediately, with the chives scattered over.

Sautéed Mushrooms and Fresh Mozzarella

Cheese Roll Sandwich

Panino alla Funghi *Among the enticing, freshly made sandwiches, offered by Italian cappuccino bars, are ones filled with meat, fish, salads, and vegetables.*

pizzas and bread dishes

Serves 4

- 8–12 oz common cultivated mushrooms, sliced
- 2 Tbsp olive oil, plus extra for drizzling
- 2 garlic cloves, chopped
- salt, to taste
- a large pinch of thyme
- 4 crusty French or sourdough rolls, split into halves
- 7 oz mozzarella cheese (including packing water), sliced

Preparation: 10 minutes

Cooking time : 5 minutes

❶ Lightly sauté the mushrooms in the olive oil with the garlic until golden brown. Season with salt and thyme, and let cool.

❷ Drizzle a little extra olive oil over the cut sides of the rolls then layer first the mozzarella cheese then the mushroom mixture. Close up and enjoy.

This whole book is awash in sauces: delicious, mushroomy, interesting sauces. Throughout, you will find plenty of cream, reductions of wine, essences of herbs, and gutsy mixtures of tomato and sausage, all coating any of the myriad types of earthy mushrooms and fungi.

Following are a handful of useful sauces for your repertoire that can go nearly anywhere.

Wild Mushroom and Chipotle Salsa

The smoky scent of chipotles deliciously sets off the woodsey, hearty flavor of wild mushrooms. Since the mushrooms are going to be overpowered to a degree, do not use anything too subtle or too expensive. I like an assortment of shiitakes, with a few mousserons, chanterelles, slices of porcini, and so forth.

The salsa is delicious with tacos, tostadas, and tortillas, or anything from the barbecue, such as barbecued corn or duck.

- 1 oz dried mushrooms or 6–8 oz fresh, including oysters, chanterelles, and other fleshy mushrooms
- ½ onion or 3 shallots, chopped
- 3 garlic cloves, sliced
- 2–3 Tbsp olive oil
- 1–2 pinches whole cumin seeds
- ¼–½ tsp mild chili powder, such as ancho
- 4 fresh ripe tomatoes or canned (plus 4–5 Tbsp juice), diced
- ½ or more chipotle chili in adobo, chopped or mashed, or a few shakes of bottled chipotle
- juice of ½ lemon or lime
- 2 Tbsp chopped fresh cilantro
- salt, to taste

Preparation: 10-15 minutes

Cooking time : 10-20 minutes

❶ Rehydrate the dried mushrooms, if using, by either soaking or simmering in hot water until tender. When cool enough to handle, squeeze dry, then chop roughly. You should have about 8 heaping tablespoons of mushrooms. If using fresh mushrooms, clean and chop roughly.

❷ Lightly sauté the onion or shallots and garlic in the olive oil, then sprinkle in the cumin seeds. Add the mushrooms, cook a few moments, then sprinkle with the chili powder. Add the tomatoes and cook until reduced to a salsa-like mixture. Then add the chipotle, lemon or lime juice, and cilantro. Add salt to taste and serve as desired.

VARIATION:

Add the kernels of two ears of corn, slightly scorched in a lightly oiled heavy-based frying pan or left over from a meal cooked on the barbecue.

Duxelles

This is the classic French paste of cooked-down mushrooms, sautéed very, very slowly, with additions of brandy, salt, pepper, and butter, until the mixture cooks down to its essence.

Use it as a spread for crostini or thin toasty canapés, or as a filling for chicken breasts, or to enrich sauces for pastas or soups. It's a good way of using up stems and odd pieces of mushroom.

Duxelles can be frozen for up to about 2 months.

- 8 shallots, chopped
- ¼ cup butter, preferably sweet
- 2¼ lb fresh mushrooms, either mixed wild, a combination of common cultivated and wild, or all one type, roughly chopped
- salt, ground black pepper, and grated nutmeg, to taste

Preparation: 10-15 minutes
Cooking time : 20-30 minutes

❶ Sauté the shallots in the butter for a minute or two, then add the mushrooms. Cook very slowly and evenly until the liquid that seeps out of the mushrooms is evaporated. Season with salt, pepper, and nutmeg, and leave to cool.

❷ For a smooth consistency, chop the mushrooms finely by hand or whiz in a blender or food processor.

❸ If you are going to freeze, place the mixture in ice-cube trays, freeze, then pop into plastic bags. Use as desired.

Mushroom Jus

This makes a small amount of intensely flavored mushroom liquid, delicious added to mustard, cream sauces, mashed potatoes, sautéed mushrooms, and gratinéed dumplings, or drizzled onto a plate as a tasty decoration, say as a necklace around risotto.

- 2 cups strained mushroom liquid
- ¼ stock cube

Preparation: 5 minutes
Cooking time : 15-30 minutes

❶ Place the mushroom liquid in a saucepan and bring to a boil. Cook over high heat until reduced by about half, then add the ¼ stock cube. Continue to boil until reduced to about ⅓ cup.

Index